THE GOOD HEALTH COOKBOOK

CAVENDISH HOUSE

It makes sense to care about food. A little basic knowledge coupled with some thought can ensure that you and your family not only eat well but eat wisely too—and this will be reflected in your overall health and fitness.

In the beginning of this book we have included some no-nonsense nutritional advice on vitamins and minerals and, just as important, on how to get the most from food by correct storing, preparing and cooking.

From page 21 onwards there are the recipe sections. Each one examines those health foods which are genuinely valuable, explains what they do for you and gives recipes associated with that particular food, plus ideas on how to include it in your diet. Use this book for your day-to-day menu planning and you will find yourself looking—and feeling—on top of the world.

Text: Sally Ann Voak
Editor: Magda Gray
Art Editor: Andrzej Bielecki
Illustrator: Sue Richards
Preparation of food for photography:
Jane Oddie

Published by Marshall Cavendish Books Ltd.
58 Old Compton Street, London, W1V 5PA

First printing 1973 (softback)
Second printing 1983 (hardback)

Printed by L.E.G.O., Vicenza, Italy

ISBN 0 86307 066 3

Contents

why eat well?

Health, happiness and good looks; all three have far more to do with the food we eat than most of us realize. A healthy diet can be the key to a lifetime of vitality and well-being, and the results of a new attitude to eating are really spectacular:

Good looks. Hair, skin, teeth and eyes can all benefit from an improved diet. And once the correct balance is obtained—excess carbohydrate and sugar being removed—there is certain to be an improvement in the figure too!

Improved health. The addition of vital vitamins and nutrients to a diet which was previously deficient in some ways, can make a big difference to the way you feel. This is particularly noticeable with those minor, nagging ailments—tiredness, irritability, constant colds, headaches.

More energy. Sluggishness and lack of energy can often be traced to some kind of diet deficiency. Irregular, badly-planned meals can lead to constipation, too. If life is beginning to be too much for you, if you never seem able to cope, then think seriously about changing your eating habits. It is so simple to add those missing 'vitality' ingredients to meals. Sometimes, just one basic change (eating more citrus fruits, for example, to step up your quota of vitamin C) can make all the difference to your life.

Better digestion. If you exist on a bland diet of over-refined foods for days and then suddenly indulge in a grand splurge at an exotic restaurant you can expect your stomach to complain. Keep your digestive system working properly all the time, with plenty of roughage—fibrous, bulky foods like bread, bran, wheat germ, raw or dried fruit and green 'stringy' vegetables which help food particles on their way. Then your system will be better able to cope with the unexpected.

None of this means that you have to be faddy about food. What it does mean is that you need the basic nutritional knowledge to enable you to select the best possible foods from the vast choice available. It is more useful to know what to choose from your supermarket shelf than it is to understand the differences between organic and intensive farming methods.

Basic, everyday family menu-planning is more important than preparing a grand dinner party. Day-to-day food is what actually keeps the family in top form; so it's just as important to make sure that you cook food in a way which does not kill all the goodness before it reaches the table as it is to be able to make it look appetizing.

Nutritional know-how

Because eating is a social pastime as well as a basic necessity it is sometimes difficult to relate food intake to actual body chemistry. A delicious cheese soufflé which melts on the tongue may sound positively dreary if broken down into its constituents: protein, carbohydrate, fat, vitamins A, B and E. And if this is followed by a description of what these constituents actually do when they get inside the body, then the whole thing can begin to sound like a chemistry lesson. But you do need to know the basic nutritional facts so that you can relate them to your shopping, menu-planning and cooking methods.

The recipes

All these basic facts are included here. And to help you to use this information in practical ways there are recipes associated with each particular food. (For example, recipes where honey is an important ingredient follow immediately after the information about honey.)

As a further visual guide each recipe has the following symbols:

⧖ This is a guide to the preparation and cooking time required for each dish and will vary according to the skill of the individual cook.

⧖ Less than 1 hour

⧖ ⧖ Between 1 hour and 2½ hours

⧖ ⧖ ⧖ Over 2½ hours

☆ This indicates that the recipe requires no cooking

How to read the charts

Charts which set out the nutritional values of foods are included throughout. The weight measurement used for all the foods in these charts is 100 grams. The amounts of protein, fat and carbohydrate contained in the foods are expressed in grams (g.). The minerals and vitamins in milligrams (mg.). (There are 1000 milligrams to a gram.) So looking at the flour chart (see page 62) you can see, for example, that for every 100 grams of wholemeal [wholewheat] bread you eat you get 8.2 grams of protein and 261 milligrams of potassium.

The only exceptions are vitamins A and D which are commonly expressed in 'International Units'. This is a form of measurement devised by the World Health Organisation and used in this way all over the world.

Remember too that some foods are very much heavier than others. An average portion of, say, Cheddar cheese usually weighs 100 grams and would therefore supply approximately the same nutrients as those mentioned in the chart. However, few people would eat 100 grams of honey at one sitting and you should take this into account when relating the information from the charts to your daily diet.

Thought for food

It makes sense to think about what you eat and make sure you get enough of the essential nutrients. Good food well-cooked not only tastes better than convenience foods but, because it gives your body those nutrients it needs to stay in peak condition, it also makes you look and feel better.

Food deterioration

What makes food 'go off'? Here are some of the things that could speed up the deterioration of food, and some hints on how to avoid them.

Bacteria
These are the most dangerous food contaminators because they can multiply at alarming rates. Although food may have been perfectly safe when it was purchased, it can become dangerously infected by certain disease-carrying bacteria within a few hours. Gastro-enteritis, food poisoning and mild intestinal troubles can usually be traced to bacteria in food, so be very careful. Never keep a meal warm for too long.

Enzymes
These are the catalysts within food which help chemical changes to take place when it is exposed to air and sunlight. Enzymes hasten the destruction of vitamins A and C in fruit and vegetables which are exposed to the air. The only remedy is to make sure that the produce is eaten quickly once it is ripe.

Yeasts
These attack sugary foods—fruit dishes, yogurt, puddings. They give that 'fizzy' taste to the food which although not harmful, is unpleasant. Do not leave sugary dishes in a warm room, or keep them for a long period in a refrigerator. (Yeasts are, of course, deliberately included in home-brewing and baking. But that's a different thing!)

food-what you need, & why

You are what you eat. This may be a simplification of the complicated processes which regulate body metabolism but even so it is basically true. Every cell in the body is made and replaced by constituents derived from the food you eat. The calcium in milk really does make and keep healthy bones and teeth, the iron in vegetables and meat really is responsible for forming healthy red blood cells.

The body is continually repairing itself, so the right kind of food is vital even for adults. And in the process of growing the right nutrients are essential to ensure healthy development.

Eating in the West is a social habit, not a daily bid for survival; most people find it difficult to appreciate the importance of the complicated process of eating which also has important emotional and psychological connections. We eat for comfort; to allay fears; to assuage guilt; because we are happy or because we are sad. These motivations can also affect the kind of food we eat—and we may choose the wrong kind.

Body metabolism

The process by which oxygen is used to convert food into energy is called the metabolic process. To understand metabolism in simple terms, imagine a series of rooms each with a connecting door to the next room. Inside each 'room' chemical changes take place involving various constituents supplied by food. Once the change has taken place, the door to the next 'room' will open satisfactorily. But it will only open if all the constituents were present. In other words, a missing mineral or a missing vitamin in the diet can impede normal metabolism. The door to that 'room' stays firmly shut, and there is a brief—or long-term—breakdown in the process.

Such a breakdown would manifest itself in something minor like splitting nails or something major like anaemia. A vegan diet, for example, comes exclusively from plant and vegetable foods and sometimes results in a lack of vitamin B12. This could lead to severe illness if the vitamin is not supplied as a supplement, for B12 is essential for building and maintaining healthy blood corpuscles.

Energy

As well as the nutrients required for growth and repair, the body also needs energy. The muscles need energy to contract and make the body work. The most important muscle of all is, of course, the heart. It pumps blood around the body. And blood carries the nutrients (taken from food) which will form and renew body cells. Then there are the muscles which control the digestive system; the nerve cells which send signals to the brain; the glands, and all the other parts of the body which have to make or do something in order to keep us alive need energy. Energy is measured in calories. Some foods supply more calories than others. Some people need more calories than others depending on their size, job (i.e. physical and mental activity) and metabolism.

Roughly half the total daily calorie intake is needed for the metabolic processes described above, the rest for physical activities and warmth. Where a person consumes food supplying more calories than he or she requires these are either 'burnt off' by a self-regulating effect of the metabolism or deposited as fat. If a person consumes food supplying fewer calories than he or she needs, the body will make up the amount needed by using fat stored. This is not harmful so long as the food which is consumed supplies the essential nutrients.

High protein Foods

A man in a moderately active job needs about 75 grams of protein a day, and a woman needs about 60. For children, the requirements vary from about 20 grams for a year-old baby, to about 70 for an active teenage boy. (Many doctors are worried that too much protein is introduced too soon into babies' diets. So check the amount required for your baby with your doctor. Young babies get all the protein they need from milk.)

Most people build their meals around the high-protein foods: meat, fish, or (in the case of vegetarians), nuts. The chart below lists 20 top protein-supplying foods. It shows the grams of protein supplied per 100 grams of the food concerned, plus grams for an average portion.

Food	Grams of protein per 100 grams of food	Grams of protein per average portion
Almonds	20.5	about 10 grams for a small handful
Bacon, gammon, fried	31.3	about 16 grams for two rashers
Beef steak, stewed	30.8	about 30 grams for an average serving
Cheese, Cheddar	25.4	about 23 grams for a 3 x 3 x 1 inch square
Cheese, Cottage	16.0	about 18 grams for a small tub or carton
Cheese, Gruyère	37.6	about 30 grams for a 3 x 3 x 1 inch square
Cheese, processed	23.0	about 4 grams for a standard portion
Chicken, roast	29.6	about 25 grams for an average serving
Cod, grilled	27.0	
Crab	19.2	about 4 grams for an average serving
Eggs, fresh, whole	11.9	about 7 grams for a medium-sized egg
Lentils, boiled	6.8	about 3 grams for a tablespoonful
Liver, Calf, fried	29.0	about 25 grams for an average serving
Milk, fresh, whole	3.4	about 9 grams for a large glass (½ pint)
Peanuts	28.1	about 16 grams for a small handful
Peas, split, boiled	8.3	about 5 grams for a tablespoonful
Pork chops, grilled,	25.3	about 5 grams for an average serving
Prawns, boiled	21.2	about 5 grams for an average serving
Sardines, canned	20.4	about 6 grams for a small tub or carton
Yogurt, low fat	4.7	

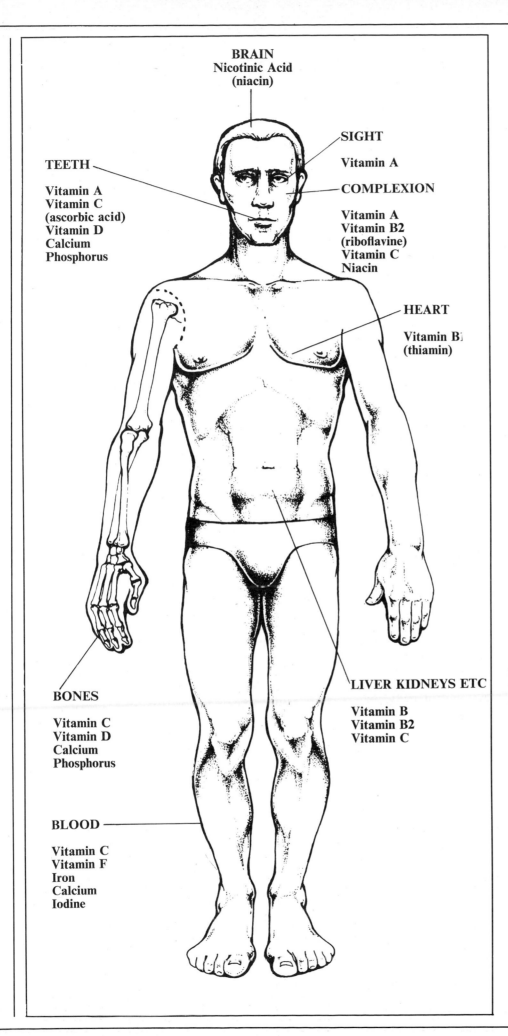

BRAIN
Nicotinic Acid
(niacin)

SIGHT

Vitamin A

COMPLEXION

Vitamin A
Vitamin B2
(riboflavine)
Vitamin C
Niacin

TEETH

Vitamin A
Vitamin C
(ascorbic acid)
Vitamin D
Calcium
Phosphorus

HEART

Vitamin B1
(thiamin)

BONES

Vitamin C
Vitamin D
Calcium
Phosphorus

LIVER KIDNEYS ETC

Vitamin B
Vitamin B2
Vitamin C

BLOOD

Vitamin C
Vitamin F
Iron
Calcium
Iodine

Vitamins and minerals

We tend to talk glibly about the importance of vitamins and minerals without considering just how recently the function of these substances was discovered. For up until the end of the nineteenth century very little work had been done to isolate the biochemical actions of the nutrients in foods. In 1753 James Lind recommended that scurvy should be treated by including lemons in the diet. This recommendation was based on observation; he did not know that citrus fruits contain vitamin C, and that scurvy is caused by vitamin C deficiency.

The word 'vitamine' was coined by a Swiss scientist named Casimir Funk at the beginning of the twentieth century. He based the name on the assumption that all these vital factors were nitrogen-containing substances called 'amines'. Later this was found to be untrue, so the 'e' was dropped from the name.

Much work is still to be done on the exact function of vitamins in the body. And research still needs to be carried out to discover just how these minute organic substances can be used in treating disease. Researches now indicate, for example, that there is a link between lack of vitamin E and heart disease. And the vitamin B complex, which contains more than 15 different substances, is also the subject of a great deal of research—particularly because the main source (the whole germ of wheat) is rapidly disappearing from Western diet.

The mineral substances in food are equally vital for in many cases they actually trigger off the action of the vitamins. Again, their importance is only just being fully realized, particularly that of the 'trace' minerals. Although these are only present in foods in minute quantities, they are essential to health. The removal of these minerals from foods during refining processes is causing much concern.

The charts over list the most important vitamins and minerals together with their functions and best food sources.

THE PRINCIPAL VITAMINS

Common name	Chemical name(s)	Good sources	Daily needs	What it does for you	Discovery date
A	Retinol	Fish liver oils, animal liver, eggs, milk, yogurt, butter, green leafy vegetables, carrots.	2.7 mg	Essential for body growth and proper function of the retina. Helps resistance to infections.	1913
B1	Thiamine, aneurine	Yeast, wheat germ, wholemeal wholewheat flour, lean meat.	1.2 mg	Essential factor in carbohydrate metabolism. Important for nervous system, digestive system and heart. Severe lack causes beriberi whick can lead to heart failure and damage to the nervous system.	1936
B2	Riboflavin	Yeast, wheat germ, liver, kidneys, cheese, meat.	1.7 mg	Important for normal growth of skin, nails and hair. Deficiency causes dull hair, split fingernails, itching eyes.	1933
B6	Pyridoxine	Yeast, wheat germ, liver, potatoes.	1.5 mg	For healthy skin and proper growth in children.	1936
	Niacin nicotinic acid,	Yeast, wheat, bread, liver, meat, fish, chicken, mushrooms.	19 mg	For healthy skin (anti-pellagra), mucous membranes and nervous system.	1937
(H)	Biotin	Yeast, peanuts, peas, mushrooms.	Unknown	Uncertain	1940
	Pantothenic acid	Yeast, liver, beans, mushrooms, peanuts.	Unknown	Uncertain	1938
	Folic acid	Yeast, liver, milk, green vegetables.	0.15 mg	Healthy blood	1944
B12	Cyanocobalamin	Liver, meat, wholemeal (wholewheat) flour, wheat germ.	0.005 mg	Healthy blood. This is known as the anti-pernicious anaemia vitamin.	1948
C	Ascorbic acid	Fresh fruit and vegetables especially citrus fruits, blackcurrants, tomatoes, rosehips.	30 mg	Vitality, resistance to infections, helps the body to resist shock, too. Essential for the formation of the body 'cement' which holds together the inter-cellular material making up the connective tissue, bones, teeth and blood-vessel walls.	1928
D	Calciferol	Fish liver oils, eggs, milk, butter, sunshine on skin.	0.01 mg	Regulates calcium and phosphorous content of the body. (This is essential in teeth and bone formation). Mostly needed during childhood but essential, too, during pregnancy.	1922
E	Tocopherol	Wheat germ, whole grains, nuts, vegetable oils.	Unknown	Protects body tissues. Keeps blood circulating freely.	1923
K		Green vegetables, liver, tomatoes, carrot tops, soya bean oil, seaweed.	Unknown	Essential for maintenance of prothrombin, one of the blood-clotting factors in blood plasma. Therefore helps to heal wounds.	1935

THE PRINCIPAL MINERALS

Common name	Chemical name	Good sources	What it does for you
Calcium	Ca	Milk, cheese, sardines or other small fish eaten whole with bones, parsley, watercress, molasses.	All body cells need calcium. Essential for the formation of bones, teeth, hair, fingernails. Protects the nervous system, helps blood clotting and is important in maintaining healthy body fluids, membrane and muscles. Particularly vital for growing children and pregnant women. (Calcium needs vitamin D to aid absorption).
Cobalt	Co	Sweetbreads, mushrooms, liver.	Constituent of vitamin B12 and concerned with the promotion of healthy nerve fibres and tissues of the bone Guards against types of anaemia.
Copper	Cu	Liver, kidney, egg yolk, lentils, wholemeal (wholewheat) flour, parsley, brown sugar, brazil nuts and walnuts.	Concerned with several enzyme systems including those responsible for the oxidation of vitamin C.
Fluorine	F	Drinking water in certain areas, seafoods, tea (particularly China tea).	Builds up tooth enamel in children and guards against tooth decay.
Iodine	I	Seafoods, Kelp, sea salt. Fruit, vegetables and cereals may contain supplies but amounts vary depending on area.	Essential for correct functioning of the thyroid gland, guards against goitre, keeps body cells and circulation active. Also assists in healthy development of the brain and continuing sexual interest.
Iron	Fe	Egg yolk, liver, black pudding (blood sausage), molasses, corned beef, peanuts, lentils and some green vegetables (e.g. watercress).	Helps make blood. During child-bearing years women need more iron than men (they lose large amounts during menstruation). Iron is also concerned with the formation of body cells and production of energy. Deficiency may cause anaemia.
Magnesium	Mg	Green salads, green vegetables, nuts, beans, lentils, whole grains.	Concerned with strength and well-being of bones, teeth, nerves, muscles, hair and nails.
Manganese	Mn	Liver, kidney, beans, lentils, cereals, tea and coffee, nuts.	Activator in a number of enzyme systems. A deficiency in animals produces poor growth and reproduction, and occasional anaemia. It can also cause bone changes and disturbances in the central nervous system and a disappearance of sexual drive.
Phosphorus	P	Milk, cheese, egg yolk, yeast, wholemeal (wholewheat) flour, nuts, meat.	Helps make bones, teeth, body cells and tissues, hair and fingernails. Helps the release of energy during the processing of carbohydrates. Phosphorus needs vitamin D to assist absorption. Many of the B group of vitamins work only when combined with phosphates in the body.
Potassium	K	Dried apricots, beans, nuts, dried currants, dates, figs, grapes, prunes, raisins, sultanas, soya flour, molasses, yeast, brown sugar.	Works with sodium to maintain a correct fluid balance. Essential for heart rhythm, nerve activity and the processing of carbohydrates.
Selenium	Se	Liver, kidney, heart.	Acts with vitamin E to maintain a healthy condition of the liver and also to inhibit the development of muscular dystrophy.
Sodium	Na	Dried apricots, beans, nuts, table salt, ham, bread, beef extract, celery, eggs, spinach,	Acts with potassium to correct fluid balance.
Sulphur	S	Nuts, dried fruits, oatmeal, barley, beans, cheese, meat,	Helps in the construction and maintenance of body cells and muscle fibres.
Zinc	Z	Oysters, sweetbreads, liver.	Involved in several enzyme systems and constituent of insulin. Eyes, teeth and testes all contain considerable amounts.

eating for health & beauty

Eating well will make the very best of your looks and could certainly help to prevent certain kinds of ill-health. Skin, hair and figure are all important beauty areas. All three need the right nutrients to look really good, and the right nutrients are supplied by food. Colds, influenza and depression are common ailments, and they can be 'treated' with food.

This deceptively simple-sounding theory can, perhaps, be best illustrated by an extreme example. Imagine two 20-year-old girls, both working as secretaries, both with 'average' characteristics: brown hair, brown eyes, slightly 'pear-shaped' figure, medium height, fairly slow-working, sluggish metabolism.

Girl A eats well. Her diet consists of fresh fruit, vegetables (good for skin, hair and figure), lean meat, fish, dairy foods and salads. She always eats a reasonably good breakfast, and takes her meals at regular times. When she goes out to dinner and eats more than usual, she restricts her carbohydrate intake the next day and eats more fruit. She drinks water, milk, a little tea and coffee and a little alcohol.

This girl looks good. Her figure is firm and trim, her face is spot-free, her hair is glossy. She has vitality and an outgoing personality. She feels good, too. Her teeth are in good shape, she gets the occasional cold, but soon shakes it off, and common ailments do not often trouble her.

Girl B eats badly. Her diet consists of snack foods: fried meals, sandwiches, cakes, confectionery, plus the occasional tray meal. She eats few fresh vegetables and little fruit. She drinks sugar-loaded soft drinks and quite a bit of alcohol. She eats very little during the day—except fattening nibbles—and has lots of fried foods during the evening. She takes little exercise.

This girl is not doing herself justice. Her skin is spotty due to lack of vitamins B and C, her hair is lank and her figure is spreading. Her teeth seem to be more 'filling' than enamel (the sugary foods attract caries-forming bacteria), and she feels sluggish and depressed. She also seems to be a sitting target for all minor diseases. Last winter, she was in bed with influenza for three weeks and then had a succession of colds. She feels too tired to bother about her appearance or her work. Her doctor says that overweight could lead to high blood pressure.

Girl A is obviously making the most of herself, Girl B isn't. Even a natural beauty would have problems staying beautiful on B's diet. At best, she would feel sluggish and below par, at worst she would have dull hair, an unattractively spotty face and a lumpy figure.

Give your body a chance to prove how good it can look and feel. Provide it with the fuel, in the form of good food, to keep ticking over nicely.

General health

Minimize the chances of succumbing to germs by making sure that your resistance is not low. Keep up your vitamin C level by eating oranges, grapefruit and green vegetables every day for vitamin C cannot be stored by the body. Doctors are concerned that modern eating habits seem to be tending to exclude sufficient quantities of the vitamin B complex. Make sure you get enough of these by drinking plenty of milk, and eating lean meat, liver, fish and some wheat germ and brewer's yeast.

Weight

Overweight really can lead to illness. Ailments which strike fat people more than lean people include heart troubles, diabetes, cerebral haemorrhage, digestive complaints and impotence. So adopting a good, well-balanced diet which is low in calories and high in essential nutrients is clearly a sensible idea.

Looks

Skin needs vitamin B2. This is present in fresh vegetables, milk and wholemeal [wholewheat] bread. Skin also needs vitamin C to purify and vitalize the blood-stream. Eat at least one orange a day, or take vitamin C supplement.

Teeth and bones need calcium and vitamin D. These are found in milk, fish oils (and the small edible bones in sardines) and yeast. Keep teeth in super health by cleaning regularly and avoiding the caries-encouraging sugary foods.

Hair is made from a protein-based substance called keratin so it needs protein and the B vitamins. (Hospitals give high protein diets to patients who have lost body hair through accidents.) A high protein diet can help your hair to grow strongly. Fish, meat, cheese, eggs and offal are all good for your hair. Yeast taken as a supplement in tablet form can also help.

Nails need protein (they, too, are keratin based), plus minerals like iodine.

Eyes need vitamin A to help to retina to function properly and to prevent night-blindness. Drink lots of water to help eyes sparkle, and eat carrots, cabbage and other green leafy vegetables, butter, eggs and fish liver oils. Avoid alcohol or stimulants like coffee and tea. These can cause red, dull eyes.

Eating for prevention and cure

Listed below are some common ailments and beauty problems, plus the foods which could help to prevent and cure them. But seek the advice of your doctor too.

Ailment or problem	Foods which can help—and why		
Common cold, influenza.	Massive doses of vitamin C have been recommended both as treatment and a preventative—two or three oranges a day, plus plenty of raw green vegetables.	Sluggish metabolism, goitre, sluggish thyroid	These are all related to thyroid gland secretion, and this depends on sufficient iodine—found in seafoods, iodized salt and kelp.
Acne.	Vitamins B and C help to keep skin clear. If your skin is blotchy and tired-looking, drink lots of water, eat citrus fruits and green vegetables	Lethargy, pale skin, anaemia.	Iron is vital for the formation of red blood cells which carry oxygen to all parts of the body. About a quarter of all women are iron-deficient. Eat liver, kidney or heart,
		Falling hair, brittle nails.	You need protein to build keratin, hair follicles and nails, together with sulphur and vitamins B and D to keep them healthy. Eat meat, fish, cheese, eggs, cabbage.
Constipation, gastro-enteritis.	Natural yogurt can help to soothe troubled stomachs and ward off infection.	Depression, insomnia.	Vitamin B1 (thiamine), B2 (riboflavin) and protein can help. Brewer's yeast is a good source.

food & sexuality

Healthy eating really can improve your sex life by providing the nutrients, vitamins and minerals which give you a desire for sexual fulfilment plus the energy and stamina to enjoy it. It may come as a surprise to know that most so-called 'aphrodisiac' foods really do contribute vital substances which play an important part in desire and fertility. These foods will not produce an overnight result, but taken regularly they can have a marked effect.

Take the 'myth' about the aphrodisiac powers of oysters, for example. Apparently, Casanova considered oysters to be so potent that he ate about 50 a day. Chemically, he could have been on to a good thing because oysters are a rich source of zinc, which encourages healthy growth and guards against anaemia. The eyes, teeth and testes all contain considerable amounts of zinc. Other traditional aphrodisiac foods—mushrooms, radishes (used as a sex food by the ancient Egyptians) and watercress—are less expensive than oysters and probably just as effective. There is no need to splurge on caviar and artichokes to guarantee a lifetime of love. A good diet of fresh and homely foods like salads, green vegetables and the cheaper cuts of meat are just as good. Even a weekly meal which includes liver—rich in vitamins A, B1, B2 and E—a salad and some fresh fruit will help to keep you sexually active. The essence of a virile body is a good diet.

Stamina

Up to 50 per cent of all women experience iron-deficiency at some time

Aphrodisiacs—fact or fiction?

Some well-known and not-so-well-known 'aphrodisiac' foods are listed below—plus a few good reasons why they may actually work!

Eggs
Iron, protein, vitamins A, B and E, phosphorus and copper are all supplied by eggs.

Oysters
These contain zinc which is present in eyes, teeth and testes, encourages healthy growth and discourages anaemia. Zinc also helps to keep skin young and supple and a deficiency can cause premature ageing.
(Zinc is also found in sweetbreads and liver.)

Liver and kidney
These may not seem romantic foods but they should be added to the list as they contain minerals like copper, manganese, zinc and iron—all of which help to stimulate sexual urges—together with vitamins A, B, C and E.

Saffron, cinnamon, pepper, peppermint, ginger
These spices that tempt the palate are also generally supposed to tempt the sexual appetite. To date, however, there is no evidence to show why they should.

Lobsters
Iodine is the 'life tempo' mineral which keeps body cells healthy and aids circulation. It also helps to keep you young and thinking about sex. Because they contain iodine lobsters are a good choice for health and sex-conscious businessmen. But, if lobster is too expensive, haddock, herring and whiting are effective substitutes.

Mushrooms
These contain vitamins B1 and B2 plus a good sprinkling of minerals. Truffles have the same qualities, and have long been trusted as an effective aphrodisiac.

Caviar
Any fish roe is an excellent source of potassium—for muscular strength, mental clarity, vitality—and other vital minerals. Cod's roe is just as good if caviar is too expensive.

Asparagus, celery, artichokes
These three vegetables are often quoted as aphrodisiacs. Certainly they are good sources of vitamins B and C, and stimulate taste buds and digestive juices. Celery is probably the most versatile, and the least expensive, of the three.

during their child-bearing years. (The worst times of all are just before and after menstruation.) Iron-deficiency makes you feel 'droopy' and below par, so an iron supplement in food or tablet form is vital if you want to stay in top form throughout each month. Meat, green vegetables—particularly watercress—and offal [variety meats] will help.

Protein is good for stamina, too. So eat lots of meat, eggs, cheese and fish.

Fertility

It has been shown that obesity can impede fertility in both men and women. Solve your weight problem and you could go a long way towards solving your fertility one, too. Quite apart from the biological factors involved, being seriously overweight is aesthetically undesirable for a full, rewarding sex-life. So fresh, lightly-cooked food is infinitely better than heavy carbohydrate-packed 'stodge' if you want to maintain a healthy interest in sex for as long as possible. Middle-age spread is a strong anti-love-making factor—keep a firm, reasonably slim body and you will keep your love-life active.

Virility

Go to bed on a full stomach at your peril. A heavy meal eaten late at night will slow down desire and responses to love-making. Nowadays, there is a tendency to eat the main meal of the day half-way through the evening, sometimes hunched over a tray watching television at the same time. This is unfortunate because both digestion and love-life can suffer. A full stomach, especially if accompanied by the effects of alcohol, will induce drowsiness.

A woman who has eaten earlier in the evening and who is ready for love at bedtime can hardly expect her man to show the same enthusiasm if she has just presented him with a huge cooked meal or a pile of sandwiches. If you must serve—or eat—a late meal make it light: a tossed salad and cold meat or fish, a slice of wholemeal [wholewheat] bread and fruit to follow. Avoid heavy sauces, pasta, potatoes, stodgy puddings and spirits.

Milky drinks are sleep-inducing, too. Why not try an energy-inducing night cap for a change? Mix 3 tablespoons natural yogurt, 8 tablespoons freshly-squeezed orange juice, 2 tablespoons honey, 1 teaspoon apple cider vinegar and a sprinkling of wheat germ flakes. Stir and drink. It tastes surprisingly good and it does you good too.

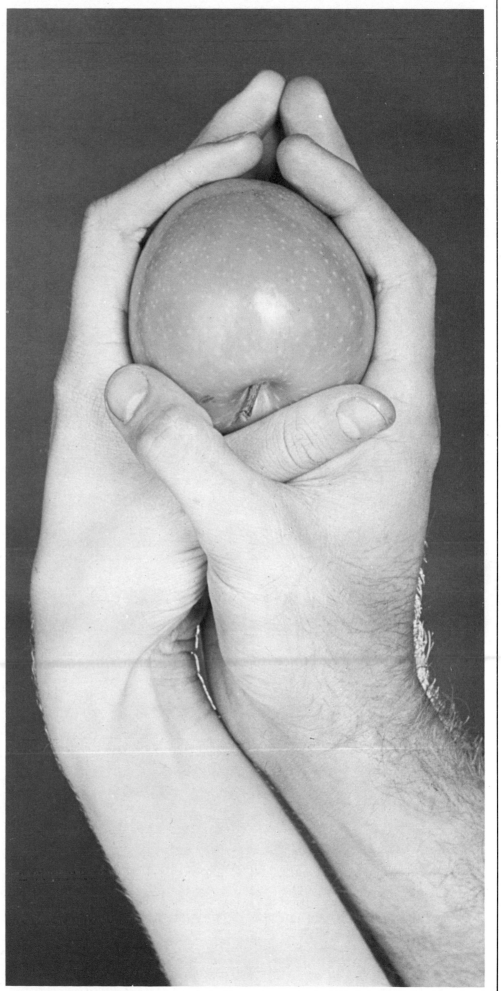

vitality diet

This one-week diet plan provides all the nutrients required for good health and good looks. Use it as a tonic when you feel below par, or when you know that your food intake has been badly balanced over the past few weeks.

Follow this diet exactly for just one week. You will find yourself feeling so much better that you will resolve to keep up the good food habits you have acquired.

Avoid alcohol during the day, but do sip mead* or wine with the evening meal, or beer if you prefer it. Spirits should be avoided when possible.

At the beginning of the diet we give you suggestions for mid-morning and mid-afternoon snacks to keep you feeling at top form when energy is flagging. After two days, however, you should feel able to go through from breakfast to lunch and lunch to the evening meal without a snack.

If you do feel hungry between meals have a piece of fresh fruit or a glass of fruit juice. This will effectively raise a flagging blood sugar level without adding the pure sucrose found in sweets, cakes and buns.

Day One
Breakfast:
Fresh, unsweetened orange juice
2 tablespoons Muesli* with milk
1 slice wholemeal [wholewheat] bread*
   with a little butter and honey
Decaffeinated coffee with milk, no
   sugar

Mid-morning:
1 glass vegetable juice* (choose any
   one of the recipes)

Lunch:
Cottage cheese lunch platter*
1 banana
Large glass milk

Mid-afternoon:
1 orange

Evening meal:
Chicken with tarragon sauce*
Buttered spinach
1 slice wholemeal [wholewheat] bread*
   with a little butter
Fig and apple pie*

Day Two
Breakfast:
Unsweetened tomato juice with 1
   teaspoon wheat germ stirred in
1 egg, boiled, with 1 slice bran bread
   and butter
1 orange
Decaffeinated coffee with milk, no
   sugar

Mid-morning:
1 dish yogurt* mixed with dried fruit
(raisins, chopped apricots, etc.)

Lunch:
Lemon consommé with yogurt*
Cottage cheese and
   mushroom quiche*
Bean salad*
Large glass milk

Mid-afternoon:
1 glass vegetable juice (choose any
one of the recipes)

Evening meal:
Baked cod* with watercress dressing*
Date and orange salad*
1 slice banana nut bread* with a
little butter

Day Three
Breakfast:
Yogurt with orange whip*
1 slice wholemeal [wholewheat] bread*
   with a little butter and honey
Decaffeinated coffee with milk, no
   sugar.

Lunch:
Onion soup*
Braised beef rolls with beans*
Small bunch grapes
Large glass orange juice

Evening meal:
Liver with basil*
Green salad
Date and orange salad*

Day Four
Breakfast:
1 dish yogurt* with 1 tablespoon honey
   and a sprinkling of wheat germ
Compôte of fresh fruit
1 slice wholemeal [wholewheat] bread*
   with a little butter
Decaffeinated coffee with milk, no
   sugar

Lunch:
Chicken casserole*
Watercress and carrot salad*
1 slice wholemeal [wholewheat] bread*
   with a little butter
1 orange
Tea with lemon

Evening meal:
Pizza with cheese and olives*
Slice of banana nut bread*

Day Five
Breakfast:
1 egg, poached, on 1 slice of wholemeal
   [wholewheat] bread*, toasted
Stewed prunes
Decaffeinated coffee with milk, no
   sugar

Lunch:
Clear vegetable soup with cheese and
   yogurt*
Sliced cold meats with Cole slaw
   salad*
Honey raisin pudding*
Large glass orange juice

Evening meal:
Baked stuffed mackerel*
Crunchy winter salad with piquant
   dressing*
1 orange

Day Six
Breakfast:
Unsweetened grapefruit juice
Herb omelette made from 1 egg with
   mushrooms
1 slice wholemeal [wholewheat] bread*
   with a little butter
Decaffeinated coffee with milk, no
   sugar

Lunch:
Braised beef rolls with beans*
Coconut apples*
Large glass milk

Evening meal:
Smoked fish and cottage cheese
   cocottes*
Moroccan vegetable couscous*
Honey biscuits*

Day Seven
Breakfast:
Unsweetened tomato juice with 1
   teaspoon wheat germ stirred in
1 egg, boiled, with 1 slice bran bread
   and butter
1 apple
Decaffeinated coffee with milk, no
   sugar

Lunch:
Avocado rice salad*
1 small piece cheese
Large glass milk

Evening meal:
Brazil nut salad*
Fish fillets, Spanish style*
Crispy salad* with mayonnaise*
Date and orange salad*

how to get the most from food

The way you prepare and cook food is just as important as the way you select it. There is little point in shopping around for the freshest fruit, vegetables and meat and then destroying much of their nutritional value by bad storage, bad preparation and, finally, over-cooking. Many cooks are guilty of all these things, although their meals may be delicious and palatable.

Buying food

Food starts to deteriorate from the moment it leaves its original source. So it is important to buy fresh produce as near that source as possible. Once food is caught up in the warehouse—wholesaler—retailer—consumer process important nutrients can be lost. This is particularly true of fresh fruit and vegetables. Vitamin C is very volatile. Enzymes in the plants themselves cause this vitamin to combine with oxygen in the air, lowering the vitamin level in the plant. So long periods of storage in warehouse or shop mean a poor deal in terms of food-value for the consumer. Growing your own produce is one solution to this problem (see page 64). Alternatively, find a reliable retailer or buy direct from the grower.

Food storage

Ideally, food should be stored for as short a time as possible. If you can shop every day so much the better. But many people find it more convenient to shop two or three times a week, or even weekly. In this case, careful storage of fresh food becomes vital. Here is a guide to help you keep it in prime condition.

Fruit and vegetables Store these in a cool, dark place. Light can accelerate the rate at which vitamin C is lost. The enzymes which cause the destruction of vitamins A and C cannot act when the food is chilled so the refrigerator is the ideal place to keep fruit and vegetables. (Produce with heavy peel—bananas, oranges, potatoes—are the exceptions as the peel gives a certain amount of protection from oxygen.) Never keep vegetables in the refrigerator for too long. If you do the moisture in them will start to dry out. And never store fruit and vegetables too close to the freezer section or the moisture will freeze and ruin the produce.

Meat and fish Buy meat and fish as close to the time of consumption as possible. Store it at the top of the refrigerator, near the freezer section. This is particularly vital in the case of offal [variety meats], minced [ground] meat, sausages, all fish and poultry. Anything purchased frozen should be kept frozen until you are going to use it, and then allowed to thaw slowly and thoroughly before cooking. Never cook partly-frozen meat or fish, and never re-freeze it once it has thawed.

Milk and milk products If milk is allowed to stand on the doorstep in sunshine for two hours half its vitamin B2 (riboflavin) content will be destroyed. To preserve nutrients place milk, and milk products such as yogurt and cream, in the refrigerator as quickly as possible; use them the same day if you can.

Eggs Eggs are best used in cooking when they are at room temperature, so it is unnecessary to keep them in the refrigerator. They are a very valuable food. Five eggs a week provide one person with 16 per cent of the recommended intake of vitamin D, 8 per cent of that of vitamin B2 and 7 per cent of that of both iron and vitamin A. These nutrients stay intact while the egg is fresh, so consume eggs quickly. (One word of warning, however: eggs are high in cholesterol which is believed to be linked with some forms of heart disease.)

Bread and flour-based foods Keep bread covered in a dry, cool part of the kitchen. Damp will encourage mould but, on the other hand, a hot, dry atmosphere will make the bread go stale quickly. Do not throw away bread simply because it has become a little dry. Toast it instead. Bread toasted golden brown loses little of its vitamin content and becomes easier to digest.

Other foods Remember that canned and dried foods do not necessarily have an unlimited life. Canned ham and pork products should be used within six months, and no canned food should be kept in damp surroundings which could cause the cans to go rusty. (And never leave food in an opened tin. If you do not use all of it at once put the remainder in a bowl and store it in the refrigerator.)

The same rules apply to dried foods. Excessive moisture could cause the reconstitution of products such as dried peas or dried fruit to begin, and then deterioration could take place in just the same way as it would with the fresh equivalent. Flour, sugar, coffee and tea should always be kept in air-tight containers in a dry, warm place—near the stove, perhaps.

Pots and pans for healthy cooking

Iron cooking pots may have been heavy and difficult to clean, but they did have one distinct advantage: iron-deficiency was largely prevented by people actually eating bits of cooking pot. Iron pots and pans have now largely been replaced by lighter, labour-saving metals which often have a non-stick coating for easy washing. These newer metals have been criticized for possible food-contamination.

Aluminium, for example, is a soft metal which combines with food which is cooked in it or left to stand in it for long periods of time. Two toxins, aluminium hydroxide and aluminium oxide, may then be taken into the system when the food is eaten. Most aluminium pans are meant for quick cooking—boiling vegetables, etc. Use them this way, never leave food standing in them and there is no danger. Flame-proof earthenware pots and casseroles are the best choice for long, slow cooking.

Non-stick coating materials may also be suspect. When the resin coating is heated to high temperatures fumes are released which may be toxic. However, really high temperatures may also damage the surface so it is wise to use these pans on gentle or moderate heat.

Earthenware or non-enamelled iron are the safest materials for casseroles. There is a danger that enamelled

casseroles could contaminate food, especially if the lid is coloured red, yellow or orange or if there is a design on the underside of the lid and the inside of the pot. The coloured enamel used could contain lead or cadmium, and when cooking starts, and the steam condenses inside the pot and under the lid, small quantities of these two poisons could drip into the food. Lead poisoning has been linked with brain damage and cadmium with kidney trouble. But this danger only exists if it is an old pot and food is eaten from it regularly. (Manufacturers have stopped using enamel containing these poisons so this warning does not apply to new casseroles.) If you suspect that one of your cooking pots may be contaminated, use it with greaseproof [waxed] paper or foil under the lid, and throw this away after cooking.

Washing up

It is vital to clean all pans thoroughly after use, particles of old food left in the pan and re-heated when you next use it may encourage bacteria which could spread to the food being freshly cooked.

Wash and clean cutlery properly, paying particular attention to forks which sometimes trap particles of food between the prongs. And do make sure that the cutlery drawer is cleaned regularly. There is no point in putting shining utensils back in a dirty, germ-ridden cupboard.

If you have a dish-washer, clean the filter every day according to the manufacturer's instructions, scrub the racks and cutlery holders from time to time. Finally, clean the sink itself thoroughly at least once a day, sprinkling a good disinfectant down the waste-pipe and drain. Germs love sinks, dish-cloths, dish-mops, scourers and all the associated kitchen paraphernalia.

Food preparation

Paradoxically, an excess of hygiene can be a dangerous thing, particularly in the preparation of food. If this sounds unlikely consider the cook who ruthlessly strips away the outside leaves of vegetables, thoroughly soaks what remains in salted water and perhaps even leaves them in the water until cooking time. Vegetables treated in this way will certainly be clean, but valuable vitamins and minerals will be lost. (Vitamins B and C are soluble in water.) The rule for all food preparation is to be thorough but quick.

Meat Wash meat quickly under a cold tap, dry it thoroughly and then cook it. Never soak meat. Do make sure that frozen meat—particularly chicken—is completely thawed before cooking, but do not leave the thawed meat standing in a warm room for long. Where meat is to be trimmed or cut up for a specific dish try to preserve the blood which drains off as this contains a high proportion of the iron content.

Fish Scrape the scales off both sides of the fish under running water; use a knife and work from the tail towards the head. Remove entrails from round fish by making a slit from the gills half-way to the tail, drawing out the insides and cleaning away any blood. Flat fish, such as sole and plaice [flounder], should be slit through the cavity which lies in the upper part of the body under the gills. Then the entrails can be cleaned out in the same way. Cut off gills, fins, head and tail if desired, rinse quickly again and then cook.

Fruit and vegetables Do not discard peelings and outside leaves on vegetables. If possible, leave them on. Most young green vegetables have tender outside leaves, and these often contain the greatest concentration of nutrients. Never discard the tough ones either. Keep a special bag or pan for carrot, radish and celery tops, pea-pods and the outer leaves of lettuce, cabbage, spinach and cauliflower. These can be the basis of a really good soup stock.

Fruit is best eaten raw, peel and all, but when you intend to cook it remember not to soak it in water beforehand. Fruits which have a thick peel—oranges, grapefruit and lemons—will obviously have to be peeled. But the peel is delicious grated and added to the final dish.

Potatoes and other root vegetables should be washed quickly but thoroughly and, if possible, cooked without being peeled. The peel can be easily removed before serving. The minerals are often concentrated just below the skin and are lost if the vegetable is peeled thickly. (New potatoes are, of course, delicious eaten skin and all.) If you want to prepare vegetables in advance, wash and dry them thoroughly and store them in a plastic bag or container in the refrigerator. Never leave vegetables in a saucepan for hours before you cook them.

Salads Wash salad vegetables quickly in running water and make sure they are dried properly before any dressing is applied. This is necessary for two reasons. First, the dressing will not adhere to the leaves if they are wet. Secondly, valuable vegetable juices could be drawn out into any available moisture when salt is added to the finished dish. Keep salad vegetables in the refrigerator. Never leave them floating in the sink.

Store cupboard check list

Here is a guide to basic foods which give excellent nutritional value, retain their flavour and have store-cupboard lasting power. You can find all these in your supermarket. Add a few items each week to your shopping list and build up a good stock of ingredients for healthy meals then you won't have to worry if you don't have time to shop.

Canned foods	Food value
Pilchards, sardines herrings, tuna	Vitamins A and D, protein, calcium, potassium
Corned beef	Protein, iron.
Soups	Some protein and iron; a good source of minerals like chlorine and sodium

Frozen foods	
Vegetables	Vitamins A (carrots) B and C.
Fruit juices (unsweetened)	Vitamin C.
Fish	Protein, minerals, some vitamin B.

Dried foods	
Milk (whole, unskimmed)	Vitamin A, B, C and D, protein, fat.
Fruit	Vitamin A and minerals. especially potassium.

Cereals	
Unpolished, whole grain rice	Vitamins B and E.
Flour, wholemeal (wholewheat)	Vitamins B and E.
Muesli	Protein vitamins B and E,
Pasta	Vitamin B

Fresh foods with lasting power	
Bananas	Vitamins A, B, C, D and E plus minerals, especially chlorine. (Buy them green and let them ripen at home).
Oranges, grapefruit	Top source of vitamin C. Keep in a cool place.
Potatoes	Minerals, vitamins A, B and C.

16

Comparative Food Values

Here are some popular foods—fresh and canned—compared to see which provided the best food value. The nutrients in branded foods will, of course, vary according to preparation methods so the figures given are taken from the average food-values of various popular brands.

	Protein	Carbohydrate	Vitamin B1 (thiamine)	Vitamin B2 (riboflavin)	Nicotinic acid	Vitamin C (ascorbic acid)
			mg. per 100 grams			
Peas, fresh and frozen, boiled	5.0	7.7	0.25	0.11	1.5	15
Peas, dried, boiled	6.9	19.1	0.11	0.07	1.0	Trace
Peas, canned	5.9	16.5	0.12	0.07	1.0	Trace

Best buy: frozen or fresh peas supply most-vitamin B and C and least carbohydrate.

Soup	Protein (grams per 100 grams)	Iron (mg. per 100 grams)
Lentil soup, homemade	5.3	0.10
Tomato soup, canned	0.9	0.30
Vegetable soup, canned	1.9	0.44
Chicken Noodle soup, dried mix	13.3	2.84

Best buy: although canned tomato soup is universally the best seller, dried chicken noodle soup provides twelve times more protein.

Canned Meat:	Protein	Iron
	mg. per 100 grams	
Corned beef	22.3	9.8
Chopped ham	15.2	1.5
Luncheon meat	11.4	1.1

Best buy:
corned beef gives more protein, so is a better choice for a main meal source than the other two.

Cooking

The shorter the cooking time, the less vitamins are lost. But the way you cook food, and the time it is kept hot before serving, are also vitally important. Large-scale caterers who have to keep food hot for long periods are, probably unwittingly, depriving their customers of nutrients. So if you have to eat in a restaurant or canteen every day, do not rely on those bulk-prepared vegetables for your daily supply of vitamin C.

Boiling It is never a good idea to boil food for long periods. Try to cut down the time that vegetables, meat or fish are boiling in liquid, use a very little water or stock and cover the pan so that vitamins and minerals do not disappear in steam. All minerals, sugars, vitamin C and all the B complex vitamins are soluble in water, even when the food is raw. During boiling all nutrients, including those which do not dissolve in water, will gradually pass into the cooking liquid. Use that cooking liquid to make gravies or broths even if only a few tablespoons are left.

There is a theory that the greatest loss of vitamins from food occurs between the time that the food is put on the heat and the time when it reaches boiling point, so try to shorten this period as much as possible.

Steaming This can help to reduce vitamin loss if it is carefully done. If possible, buy a steamer—a pan with a wire basket inside which holds the vegetables above the water-level in the pan.

If you don't have a steamer however, you can still steam leafy vegetables. Put two or three tablespoons of water into the pan, cover and boil until the pan is filled with steam. The steam will then replace the oxygen which usually destroys vitamins A and C. Add the vegetables quickly, cover the pan again and cook the food as quickly as possible. It is vital that the steam should be kept inside the pan throughout the cooking period. And remember to use any liquid left after cooking for gravies and broths.

'Short' cooking The Chinese and Japanese have this technique down to a fine art, and it is an excellent way of preserving the nutrients in vegetables, meat and fish. Chop the food finely and then cook it quickly in a pan with a little vegetable oil to prevent it sticking. For dinner parties this can be done over a spirit stove at the table.

The only possible disadvantage to this method is that breaking up food does increase the surfaces exposed to oxygen, and so may accelerate the deterioration of vitamins. The answer is to chop, shred or grate the food immediately before cooking it.

Grilling [broiling] and frying Overcooking meat will destroy vitamin B1. And leaving the juices in the pan will cut down the iron content of the meal. So do keep grilled [broiled] and fried dishes rare, and use the juices for gravies or soups. Grilling [broiling] is also a good way of cooking fish.

Roasting and baking These are both good ways of cooking foods as long as you do not add too much extra fat. Wrap food in aluminium foil or transparent wrap so that it can cook in its own juices. And keep the delicious juices for gravies or stock.

Leftovers

Do not re-heat vegetables. Double cooking, plus possible keeping-warm time will destroy a very high proportion of the vitamin C content. Meat stews and broths can, however, be re-heated without much loss of nutrients because these are largely contained in the liquid surrounding the meat. Make sure they are thoroughly cooked however. Meat dishes that are re-heated should be brought to the boil quickly and boiled fast for 2-3 minutes, stirring constantly with a wooden spoon to avoid burning. Reduce the heat and simmer for 15 minutes. This ensures that any bacteria are destroyed.

The stockpot

Use leftover bones, poultry carcasses, fish pieces and vegetables to make nutritious stock—so useful as a base for many soups, sauces and stews. Brown meat bones in the oven, then put them in a large, heavy-bottomed pan with plenty of water. Add a few carrots, onions, turnips or other root vegetables, whole peppercorns and herbs. Bring to the boil and then simmer for 2-3 hours. This meat-based stock will keep for 3-4 days if you keep topping it up and boiling it every day—after that, discard it and start afresh. Fish and vegetable stocks can be made in the same way, without browning in the oven first. However, note that fish stocks, and stock which contains any green vegetables, should be used the same day, as they sour very quickly.

Salt and pepper

Use crystalline sea salt for cooking and at the table. Its main advantage used to be the iodine and other minerals which were usually removed from refined table salts. Nowadays, most table salts are iodized, so sea salt's pleasing texture and fresh taste are now its major recommendations. Use it with freshly ground black peppercorns for all your cooking needs.

re-think eating habits

There is no doubt that eating habits have deteriorated considerably over the last few years. It is this, rather than factory farming or food processing, which is primarily to blame for bad nutrition. After all, one helping of processed canned peas is hardly likely to hurt anyone. It is when those peas become the only green vegetable served at any meal that there is cause for concern. And, sadly, more and more people are depriving themselves of essential nutrients either through laziness, lack of interest or sheer ignorance.

Lack of time

Many people do not have a good, mixed diet. Instead, they subsist on hastily-prepared convenience foods, starchy snacks and confectionery. If they ate properly instead, then perhaps the cry for the preservation of minerals and vitamins in foods would be unnecessary. You can hardly blame manufacturers for producing the kind of goods that people want. Nor can you blame them for the fact that people are using items meant as useful additions to a diet as staple foods. (When the first frozen peas were marketed no one envisaged that a whole generation of children might grow up not knowing what a fresh pea tasted like!) But the manufacturers are, perhaps, encouraging the steady increase in bad eating habits with clever advertising.

Time rather than lack of money seems to be the main excuse for bad eating habits. Even an affluent family may be eating badly—particularly if the mother is too tired to shop daily for fresh produce. Here are some ideas to overcome this problem.

Shopping

If you work, shop once a week for main store-cupboard foods, weekend meat and bread. Use lunch-hours for buying fresh produce. Buy in small amounts that are easy to carry home—that way they will be fresher, too.

Cooking

Plan meals ahead—a week's menus at once if possible. To give yourself a proper rest have a mid-week roast and plan a cold picnic for the weekend. Prepare vegetables in advance if necessary and store in plastic bags in the refrigerator. They are just as quick to cook as canned or frozen vegetables. Use evenings or a free weekend to prepare a few nutritious snacks that the family can eat when you are not there to cook: open flans, wholemeal [wholewheat] scones, homemade soups, fresh fruit juices. Then, they will not be tempted in your absence to eat crisps [potato chips], sweets, sugary fruit drinks, etc.

Convenience foods

These are usually taken to mean the mass-produced, instant foods, but there are some superb natural foods which could just as well be called convenience foods. Milk is possibly the most convenient food of all. And fish is easy and quick to prepare when there is no time to cook a meat dish. Apples, bananas and oranges all travel well, need no special container and are fun to eat. Eggs come in their own extremely convenient packaging, and can be cooked in just three minutes. So there is no excuse for anyone to argue that they don't have the time to eat correctly.

Meal-times

Encourage the family to treat at least one meal of the day as a social occasion when they meet for a leisurely meal around a table. Avoid the tray meal

---

10 rules to help you break those bad eating habits

1. Eat a good breakfast every day, and make sure it supplies protein.
2. Never miss a meal.
3. Overcome a sweet tooth.
4. Pre-plan meals when possible.
5. Have nutritious snacks available for times when you cannot cook.
6. Be sure to buy fresh foods—fruit, vegetables, meat, fish—whenever possible.
7. Be aware of advertising pressure to buy confectionery and starchy foods, but do not succumb to it.
8. Make time to enjoy your food. Don't rush meals.
9. Plan your shopping list. Do not just dash around a supermarket selecting random items.
10. Remember that your example could influence others, especially children.

---

eaten in front of the television. If the family is in a rush, serve a really nutritious main course—a casserole, say—and fruit or cheese for dessert.

The dangers of refined sugar

In the West we now eat 20 times as much sugar as 200 years ago. The total yearly consumption is now around 45 pounds per head, a very large proportion of this being contained in manufactured foodstuffs—soft drinks, cakes, confectionery, ice-cream and baby foods. It could be argued that sugar supplies energy—and is therefore an important requirement in a healthy diet. However the word 'sugar' can be applied to various substances with similar, but not identical, properties. Some of the best known are glucose, fructose, maltose, lactose and sucrose. Sucrose is the substance which is found in refined table sugars and in sweetened foods. Glucose is found in fruits and vegetables, and is a key material in body metabolism. Sucrose, like glucose, converts rapidly into energy (i.e. converts into blood sugar), but it is usually stored as fat for future use because adequate supplies of sugar are found in fruits and some vegetables. And these foods have the advantage of providing vitamins and minerals as well as energy. Pure sugar provides energy but nothing else. And it is bad for your teeth and your figure too.

Fats—do you need them?

The dietary habit of always spreading butter or margarine on bread is peculiar to Western countries—where fat intake is usually above a healthy level, leading to overweight and possibly heart disease. The trouble is that the 'visible' fats—butter or margarine, fat on meat, lard, suet—make up only half the daily fat intake. The rest is 'invisible' fat supplied in the foods like eggs, cheese, milk, peanuts and some fish.

Fats are necessary as a concentrated source of energy. They build body fat to insulate against cold and give a protective, cushioning effect around some internal organs. And certain constituents of vegetable oils, the essential fatty acids, are necessary for correct growth and healthy skin.

What you must avoid is an excess of fat—vegetable or animal—which could lead to obesity problems. There is, too, a danger in the intake of too much saturated fat. This is found in animal fats and dairy products: meat, lard, butter and margarine.

Vegetable oils—why they are better for you

Excessive quantities of cholesterol (hard fatty acids) and triglycerides (soft, buttery, fatty acids) can cause a build-up of fat in the blood and sometimes a blockage in the arteries. However, liquid, polyunsaturated fat is found in certain vegetable oils, sunflower seed and margarine made only from these oils. This fat does not produce a fatty acid build-up. The sensible way to include the best kinds of fat in your diet is to make sure that milk, eggs, lean meat, vegetables and vegetable oils figure strongly. If you have a family history of heart disease, or are in the 'danger' age-group of forty-plus, then it is wise to cut down on animal fats and use margarine made entirely from polyunsaturated fats. If you tend to be overweight, then avoid all the visible fats—your health will improve.

Liquid refreshment

Water-based drinks—tea, coffee and diluted soft drinks—are not as good for you as plain water. In fact, by mixing in popular beverage additions to water, you are simply adding your own toxins! Tannin (in tea) and caffeine (in coffee) are artificial stimulants which encourage acid secretion in the stomach which can, in turn, produce ulcers. They inhibit normal vitamin B metabolism and are definitely addictive! Scientists recently researching the stimulative effects of coffee on a group of students found that they experienced definite 'withdrawal' symptoms when supplies of the beverage were cut off. Headaches, dizziness and bad concentration ensued. Gradually, the symptoms passed and all subjects ultimately felt better without the artificial 'kick' of coffee.

Sweet drinks just load pure carbo-hydrate into perfectly good water. They leave that sticky residue on the teeth which encourages dental caries, and their extra calories add inches.

The water-drinking habit is a good one. Add herbal teas and pure fruit and vegetable juices to your daily total fluid intake, and try to cut down consumption of tea and coffee.

The best alcoholic drinks in terms of food-value are beer, stout, mead (see p. 55) and red wine. Spirits supply little except calories! Beer and stout have the advantage of being rich in the 'B' vitamins (contained in the yeast with which they are made), plus a little protein, plenty of carbohydrate and minerals like potassium and chlorine. In fact, these are a good food choice, as long as the calories they supply are taken into account when the rest of the day's meals are planned. (For weight-watchers, champagne and dry red or white wine are the best choices.)

vitamin pills- do you need them?

If you eat properly then food supplements should be unnecessary. But who eats properly all the time? Even the most dedicated healthy foods addict must have the occasional glaring gaps in his or her nutritional programme:

the day when work pressures were too high to go out and buy an orange at lunchtime; the evening when friends came and there was no time for a cooked supper; the Sunday when the milkman forgot to call, and so it goes on.

It is, unfortunately, not really practical to give people a list of balanced, healthy foods and say piously; 'Stick to that every day and you'll never need to take a vitamin pill.' Most people, however well-intentioned, have at some time had a bout of bad eating that amounted to virtual malnutrition! One reason for such a lapse could be emotional. A sudden craving for sweet foods after a disagreement at home could mean the psychological association of sweet things with love. And psychologists say that people will often turn to foods they actually dislike in times of emotional crisis. So the 3-day chocolate and cake eating which hits a usually food-conscious teenager after an unhappy love-affair may be a subconscious reflex which is virtually impossible to control. In such a situation it is no good saying that he or she must eat an orange and some meat to keep going. It is far better to produce a couple of vitamin pills and keep quiet until the crisis passes.

Then, too, built-in likes and dislikes can lead to diet deficiency. A pregnant woman who hates milk, cheese and yogurt will certainly suffer if her calcium intake is not bumped up with pills—even though she is a model of nutritional excellence when it comes to her weekly ration of liver and those daily green vegetables.

Men often suffer from vitamin C deficiency without even realizing it. They probably adore a huge steak with all its iron-rich juices and like a good cheese for dessert, but how many of them eat oranges or really enjoy green vegetables? If they seem to suffer from regular colds lack of vitamin C has probably a great deal to do with it. A daily pill could be a simpler, more effective, answer than persuading them to change their eating habits.

The trouble is that the water-soluble vitamins—C and B complex—must be taken daily. Five oranges on Monday will not, unfortunately, produce enough vitamin C to last until Friday. You need an orange every day, or a vitamin C pill. Check back with the chart of vitamins and minerals on pages 6-7, and remember that they are the minimum requirements. Now think back on what you ate yesterday. Did you really eat enough of everything? If not, a supplement might have been a good idea. This advice may seem to contradict what has been said previously. But people do need an escape clause. You may have firm intentions of eating well all the time, but it just is not possible to do so. Emotions, personal taste, or circumstances can, singly or together, ruin the most carefully thought-out diet ideas

Do, however, be selective about supplements. Do not bother with all-embracing 'tonic' medicines or pills unless you are sure they are supplying sufficient quantities of the things which you lack. When you swallow a pill know what it contains and why you need it.

Check, and if you find you omit the food, take the pill. **1.** *Iron: in meat and eggs.* **2.** *Vitamin E: in whole wheat and grain cereals.* **3.** *Kelp: in sea foods.* **4.** *Vitamin B complex: in dairy produce and kidneys.* **5.** *Calcium: in milk, cheese and yogurt.* **6.** *Vitamin A: in vegetables, offal and dairy products.* **7.** *Vitamin C: in green vegetables and citrus fruit.*

meat & poultry

Meat is one of the most vital sources of protein (about 27 per cent of the Western protein intake comes from it). Most families include at least one substantial meat dish in the day's meals, but all too often this takes the form of a grill or roast. Supermarkets are tending increasingly to eliminate the highly nutritious cheaper cuts of meat from their displays simply because people are not buying them. These cuts do require a little more preparation but as they help to vary the diet they are worth the effort. Badger your butcher or supermarket manager into providing these cheaper cuts and look for handy meat extras like beef bones to use for stocks, stews and soups. Gravies and sauces to accompany meat dishes are very important. They should be made with the meat juices in the pan as these contain much of the valuable iron content. Throw them away and you throw away nourishment. Roast meat in aluminium foil or a special closed roasting dish to preserve the flavour and juices, and always cover casseroles tightly. Buy meat near the time it is to be eaten—the same day, if possible. If you have to buy frozen meat, make sure it is thoroughly de-frosted before use. Eating chicken which has not been properly thawed and thoroughly cooked can give you salmonella food poisoning.

Fairly bland-tasting meats like veal and the rather dull frozen chickens that most supermarkets sell can be considerably livened with a spice or herb-based marinade. The nutritional value of a battery chicken is the same as a free-range one but the taste certainly is not, so marinating may become an everyday cookery trick rather than a special-occasion one.

Offal [Variety Meats]

Liver, kidney and other offal [variety meats], like sweetbreads, brains, tongue and heart, are all highly nutritious. They contain vitamins A, the B complex and E (an important vitamin with few good sources), plus valuable minerals. Nutritionists recommend that liver should be included in the diet at least once a week especially for pregnant mothers and children. The trouble is that many people find offal unpalatable. Tough fried liver or boring stewed kidney is not likely to bring cries of joy from your family. But if you present these meats in their most attractive forms they are both tender and flavour-ful—and you'll be able to overcome any previous resistance.

Liver tossed with Onion and Caraway Seed Roast (recipes on next pages) are high in protein and easy to prepare.

Caraway seed roast

⧖ ⧖

This dish is particularly nutritious because of the added goodness from the beef bones. Serve with dumplings or potatoes baked in their jackets.
Preparation and cooking time:
1½ hours
SERVES 4-6

2 large onions, chopped
2 tablespoons caraway seeds
sea salt
2 lb. rib or sirloin of beef (boned)
2 oz. [4 tablespoons] bacon fat or
    dripping
2 tablespoons vinegar
freshly ground black pepper
2 lb. beef bones
water

Heat the oven to 425°F (Gas Mark 7, 220°C).
Mix 2 tablespoons of the chopped onion with 1 tablespoon of caraway seeds and a pinch of salt. Spread the meat with this mixture and roll and tie it with string. Put the rest of the chopped onion and the bacon fat into a roasting tin and cook it in the oven for 5 minutes.
Reduce the heat to 375°F (Gas Mark 5, 190°C).
Put the roll of meat into the tin, sprinkle it with the rest of the caraway seeds, the vinegar, and salt and pepper to taste. Arrange the beef bones around the meat and pour in water to come a quarter of the way up. Roast in the oven for an hour basting frequently.

Chicken barbecued with white wine

Although it is simple to prepare, this chicken dish tastes delicious. Try serving with a green salad for a summer lunch.
Preparation and cooking time:
45 minutes, plus 3 hours to marinate
SERVES 4

1 tablespoon chopped fresh
    rosemary
8 fl. oz. [1 cup] olive or corn oil
¼ bottle dry white wine
the juice of 1 lemon
2-2½ lb. roasting chicken
    or 4 chicken pieces

Combine the rosemary, oil, wine and lemon. Cut the chicken into 4 pieces and marinate it in the rosemary mixture for 3 hours.

Remove the pieces from the marinade and grill them over a charcoal fire, or under a grill [broiler] for 45 minutes, brushing them frequently with the marinade.

Chicken with tarragon sauce

⧖ ⧖

Chicken—always a favourite family lunch or dinner dish—is even better with this smooth herb sauce
Preparation and cooking time:
1 hour 45 minutes
SERVES 4-6

3-3½ lb. roasting chicken
vegetable oil
2-3 tablespoons chopped fresh
    tarragon *or* 1-2 tablespoons
    chopped dried tarragon
5 fl. oz. [⅝ cup] natural yogurt
sea salt
freshly ground black pepper
a squeeze of lemon juice

Heat the oven to 375°F (Gas Mark 5, 190°C).
Roast the chicken with a little vegetable oil for 1-1½ hours or until the juices run out clear when you pierce the bird with a skewer. Add the giblets to the pan when the fat begins to collect. As the chicken roasts, sprinkle well on all sides with tarragon. When cooked, place the chicken on an oven-proof dish and keep hot.
Pour the pan juices off into a small bowl, removing the giblets. Skim off most of the fat. Stir in the yogurt. Stand the bowl over a saucepan of hot water and heat gently. Season to taste with more tarragon, salt and pepper and a dash of lemon juice. (Prepared like this, the sauce should be hot but not boiling otherwise it may curdle. If it does it may be re-mixed in a blender and then returned to the bowl.)
Pour a little of the sauce over each helping of chicken and place the remainder in a separate bowl on the table.

Goulash with dumplings

⧖ ⧖ ⧖

This dish is a variation on the traditional goulash, and is delicious served with these dumplings.
Preparation and cooking time:
5½ hours
SERVES 2-4

2 oz. [4 tablespoons] dripping
1 lb. medium-sized onions, sliced
2 garlic cloves, crushed or sliced
1 lb. lean stewing beef cut into
    cubes
1 tablespoon paprika
salt
a pinch of marjoram
½ teaspoon caraway seeds
stock
1 lb. potatoes
For the dumplings:
8 oz. [2 cups] flour
salt
2 eggs
6 oz. [¾ cup] butter
water

Heat the oven to 300°F (Gas Mark 2, 150°C).
Melt the dripping in an ovenproof casserole and fry the onions and garlic in it for 5 minutes or until golden. Add the meat and brown it quickly on all sides. Add the paprika, salt, marjoram and caraway seeds. Add the stock so that it nearly covers the meat, and cook in the oven for 4-5 hours, adding the potatoes 30 minutes before the end of the cooking time.
Make the dumplings 1 hour before the end of the cooking time.
Sift together the flour and salt and put into a bowl. Make a well in the centre, break in the eggs and stir thoroughly. Melt half of the butter and add it to the mixture. Then add enough water to make a stiff dough.
Leave the dough in a cold place for 30 minutes.
With a warm spoon cut out teaspoonfuls of the dough and cook these for 3 minutes in boiling water, then rinse them in cold water.
Just before serving melt the rest of the butter in a pan and heat the dumplings in it.

Hearts with apricot stuffing

This well-flavoured stuffing of fruit, nuts and wholemeal [wholewheat] crumbs turns an inexpensive meat into a very good supper dish.
Preparation and cooking time:
2 hours
S E R V E S 4

8 dried apricots
12 almonds, blanched and skinned
1 egg
2 tablespoons butter
1 oz. wholemeal [½ cup wholewheat] breadcrumbs
1 teaspoon sea salt
¼ teaspoon freshly ground black pepper
1 orange
4 lambs' hearts, trimmed and cleaned
2 fl. oz. [¼ cup] chicken stock
1 tablespoon sherry
To garnish:
watercress

Heat the oven to 350°F (Gas Mark 4, 180°C).
Pour boiling water over the apricots and leave them to soak for 10 minutes.
Chop or mill the almonds. Beat the egg. Melt the butter in a small saucepan. Combine these with the breadcrumbs, season with salt and pepper. Drain the apricots, snip them into small pieces and add them to the mixture. Grate in 2 teaspoons of orange zest.
Pack the stuffing into hearts, secure with small larding skewers and place in an ovenproof dish. Pour the stock over, cover and bake in the oven for 1½ hours or until the hearts are tender.
Pour the juices from the dish into a small pan and boil briskly to reduce. Squeeze the orange, add the orange juice and sherry to the pan and simmer for 5 minutes. Pour over the hearts and serve garnished with watercress.

Kidney and mushroom risotto

Unpolished rice retains the vitamins of the B complex. Cooking times are longer than for white rice, but the dish will have far more flavour.
Preparation and cooking time:
1 hour 10 minutes
S E R V E S 4

1 onion, peeled and chopped
2 tablespoons vegetable oil
2 oz. [¼ cup] butter
8 oz. [1⅓ cups] unpolished long-grain rice
1 pint [2½ cups] well-flavoured meat or vegetable stock
sea salt
freshly ground black pepper
8 lambs' kidneys, skinned and cored
4 oz. mushrooms
To garnish:
2 tablespoons chopped parsley

Melt half the butter with half the oil in a pan. Fry the onion gently in it for 5 minutes or until it is beginning to brown. Add the dry rice and continue to fry, stirring well, until the rice is golden.
Pour in three quarters of the stock. (A dash of wine or sherry could be added to the stock.) Season with salt and pepper, cover and simmer gently for 40-50 minutes. If it becomes too dry, add extra water or stock as necessary. When cooked, the rice should have absorbed all the liquid and be soft but not mushy.
Meanwhile prepare the kidneys and mushrooms. Slice the kidneys thickly and fry with the sliced mushrooms for 5 or 6 minutes over a fairly high heat in the remainder of the oil and butter. Then fork into the cooked rice, adding any pan juices.
Garnish with chopped parsley and serve.

Liver tossed with onion

Liver is made even more nutritious and tasty with this seasoning of kelp and wheat germ.
Preparation and cooking time:
20 minutes
S E R V E S 4

1½ lb. lamb or calf liver
1 large onion
3-4 tablespoons vegetable oil
1 tablespoon wholemeal [wholewheat] flour
1 tablespoon wheat germ
1 teaspoon kelp powder, or to taste
4 fl. oz. [½ cup] meat or vegetable stock
½ teaspoon yeast extract
To garnish:
watercress

Trim the liver and cut into thin strips.
Peel and slice the onion and fry in a little oil over medium heat for 5 minutes or until they begin to brown.
Mix together the flour, wheat germ and kelp. Toss the liver in the mixture. Then fry briskly in the pan with the onion for 4-5 minutes, turning occasionally, until just cooked. Transfer to a warm dish.
Add the stock and yeast extract to the pan, boil up for 2-3 minutes and pour over the liver.
Garnish with watercress and serve.

Liver with basil

The addition of basil gives a new flavour to the familiar liver and bacon.
Preparation and cooking time:
30 minutes
S E R V E S 4

1 oz. [2 tablespoons] butter
8 oz. bacon cut into strips
1 lb. lambs' liver, sliced
seasoned flour
2 tablespoons fresh chopped basil *or* 1 tablespoon dried basil
4 tablespoons red wine or stock

Melt the butter in a pan and fry the bacon. Remove it from the pan and keep warm.
Coat the liver slices in the seasoned flour and cook them in the butter for 5-7 minutes, turning all the time. Just before the liver is cooked add the basil and stock or red wine.
Arrange the liver on a plate with the bacon and pour over the pan juices.

soups and casseroles-goodness preserved

One of the main points in favour of soups and casseroles is that you eat the vitamin-rich juices, instead of draining them away. And these dishes are an ideal way of using up vegetable water which you have conscientiously refrained from pouring down the sink.

The best bases for soups are these vegetable waters containing vitamin C, stock (see p.17) and puréed vegetables like tomatoes, celery or carrots.

When selecting a lunch-time soup, remember that it should contain some protein if it is going to be the main course. So include grated cheese, beaten egg or lentils.

For slimmers, clear soups can be a good 'appetite-breaker' before the main course. They effectively take the edge off the appetite without adding too many extra calories to the meal total.

For invalids, soups are an excellent soothing introduction to solid food. But do make sure that they are nutritious as well—protein, vitamin C and iron can all be included in soup.

Once you have tasted a home-made soup the canned or powdered variety never tastes quite as good. But, when time is short, you can add your own 'extras' to patent soups: a little fresh sour cream and chopped parsley stirred into tinned lobster bisque, sherry and a few noodles added to consommé, chopped fresh tomatoes and grated cheese added to tinned tomato soup, or your own vegetable water with its valuable vitamin C residues added to a packet of dried mixed vegetable soup. These quick additions make a real difference to both flavour and goodness.

Casserole cookery is another good way of blending and conserving valuable nutrients. Even the volatile vitamin C and iron (which so often escapes in meat juices) are safely contained in a tightly-closed casserole. Slow casserole cookery is a good way of using the less expensive cuts of meat and vegetables like carrots, potatoes and onions.

You can reheat casseroles but store them in the refrigerator until you want them. Never leave them in the oven.

Chilled summertime soup

This *gazpacho*-style cold soup is particularly delicious when served with sour cream.
Preparation and cooking time:
45 minutes
S E R V E S 4

1½ lb. ripe tomatoes
10 fl. oz. [1¼ cups] chicken stock
1 large garlic clove
2 teaspoons sea salt
2 oz. wholemeal [1 cup wholewheat] breadcrumbs
4 tablespoons olive oil
2 tablespoons wine vinegar
1 large onion
½ cucumber
1 medium-sized green pepper
¼ teaspoon freshly ground black pepper
a pinch of ground cumin seed
a pinch of ground cardamom
To serve:
sour cream
toasted or fried croûtons of wholemeal [wholewheat] bread

Scald the tomatoes in boiling water and skin them. Simmer gently in the stock for 10 minutes. Reduce to a purée in a blender or food mill, then rub through a coarse sieve to remove pips.
Peel the garlic and crush well with the salt using a knife blade. Mix the garlic, salt and breadcrumbs in a bowl and add the oil and vinegar, beating well. Combine with the sieved tomatoes, cover and chill until required.
Shortly before serving, peel the onion and cucumber and wash and de-seed the green pepper. Dice them all very finely and add half to the soup. Add pepper, cumin and cardamom to taste.
Serve from a bowl set in crushed ice with the remaining chopped vegetables, sour cream and toasted or fried croûtons of wholemeal [wholewheat] bread in separate bowls.

Clear vegetable soup with cheese and yogurt

This recipe could be served alone, with a simple chopped parsley garnish or with the yogurt and cheese garnish suggested for extra protein.
Preparation and cooking time:
45 minutes
S E R V E S 6

8 oz. mushrooms
3 tablespoons butter
2 carrots
1 onion
½ celery stalk
4 oz. green beans
1½ pints [3¾ cups] stock or water
sea salt
freshly ground black pepper
6 tablespoons natural yogurt
4 tablespoons grated Parmesan cheese

Wash the mushrooms and slice thinly. Melt 1 tablespoon of butter in a saucepan, add the sliced mushrooms and cook for 2 minutes.
Clean the rest of the vegetables and cut them into thin slices. Cook in a little of the stock or water for 5 minutes. Add the rest of the stock or water, bring to the boil and simmer for about 30 minutes. Season, add the mushrooms and simmer for a further 5 minutes.
Just before serving, stir a tablespoon of yogurt into each soup portion, and sprinkle with grated Parmesan cheese.

Onion soup

This healthy, uncomplicated onion soup is delicately flavoured with herbs.
Preparation and cooking time:
45 minutes
S E R V E S 4-6

6 medium-sized onions
1 garlic clove
2 oz. [4 tablespoons] butter
1 pint [2½ cups] water, boiling
1½ pints [3¾ cups] stock, heated
1 bouquet garni
freshly ground black pepper
sea salt
1 egg, beaten
3 drops wine vinegar

Peel and slice the onions and chop the garlic. Melt the butter in a pan and add the onions and garlic. Cook them over medium heat for 5 minutes or until soft.
Pour on the boiling water, stir well, and add the stock. Put in the bouquet garni, season, and simmer for 30 minutes.
Remove the pan from the heat and take out the bouquet garni. Stir in the beaten egg and the vinegar and, serve at once.

Pork casserole

This is a satisfying dish, subtly flavoured with thyme.
Preparation and cooking time:
1¼ hours
S E R V E S 3-4

1 lb. lean pork
3 medium-sized onions
2 tablespoons butter
1 tablespoon flour
15 fl. oz. [2 cups] stock
2 celery stalks
½ teaspoon chopped, fresh thyme
   or ¼ teaspoon dried thyme
sea salt
freshly ground black pepper

Heat the oven to 350°F (Gas Mark 4, 180°C).
Cut the meat into cubes and peel and chop the onions.
Melt the butter in an ovenproof casserole and sauté the pork and onions in it until browned. Remove from the heat and stir in the flour. Pour the stock over and simmer.
Meanwhile, clean and chop the celery and then add it to the casserole with the thyme, and salt and pepper to taste. Cover and bake in the oven for about 1 hour, or until the meat is tender.

To give soups and casseroles a new look try using different combinations of flavours or unusual vegetables—celery with chicken say, or root vegetables with cheap cuts of meat.

fish

Fish is an excellent source of protein and of vitamin B (niacin). Oily fish like herring, mackerel and salmon are also good sources of vitamins A and D. Iodine comes from salt-water fish and shellfish and there is simply no other common source of it.

All this means that fish can, and should, play an important part in a well-balanced diet. Fresh fish is best for flavour, but frozen or canned fish (particularly canned oily fish) are also good buys. When shopping for fresh fish look for firm flesh, sparkling silvery scales, red gills, bright eyes and a sweet fresh smell. (Fresh fish does not smell offensive.)

Cook fish quickly. Never boil it for too long. Either poach it lightly or, for the best results, grill [broil], fry or bake in foil. Never re-heat a fish dish; eat it immediately after cooking.

The roe is the part of the fish richest in the B vitamins. It can be delicious grilled and served alone as a supper dish. Use the fish bones and heads to make fish stock. This is useful as a basis for soups and other fish dishes. Try the recipes below and experiment with your own ideas. Fish can be just as versatile as meat and it has the added advantage of being quick to cook. It generally makes a lighter dish, too, and so is often more suitable for a quick lunch than a heavy meat dish would be.

Baked cod

This is an interesting way of serving cod, and it is much better for you than frying it in batter.
Preparation and cooking time:
1 hour
S E R V E S 4-6

2 lb. cod
2 pints [5 cups] **fish stock** *or* **water**
1 **bouquet garni**
sea salt
freshly ground black pepper
3 oz. wholemeal [1½ cups wholewheat] **breadcrumbs**
3 tablespoons **flour**
2 oz. [4 tablespoons] **butter**
1 pint freshly-shelled (1 lb. frozen) **shrimps**

1 tablespoon **anchovy essence**
To garnish:
1 **lemon, sliced**
parsley

Heat the oven to 350°F (Gas Mark 4, 180°C).
Wash and dry the fish, put it in a baking tin and add the stock, the bouquet garni, salt and pepper. Mix together the breadcrumbs and flour, cover the fish with this mixture and dot with the butter.
Bake in a moderate oven, basting frequently, for about 30 minutes.
Take 4 tablespoons of the liquid out of the dish, pour it over the shrimps and mix in the anchovy essence. Pour this shrimp mixture over the fish, return it to the oven and bake for a further 7 minutes.
Garnish with lemon slices and parsley.
(For the bouquet garni use a traditional one consisting of 4 parsley sprigs, 1 thyme spray and 1 bay leaf tied together. Alternatively, try bay, fennel and lemon rind or lemon balm.)

Baked stuffed mackerel

Mackerel is a tasty and inexpensive fish, and is particularly good with this piquant stuffing.
Preparation and cooking time:
45 minutes
S E R V E S 4

4 good-sized **mackerel, cleaned and boned**
2 oz. [¼ cup] **oatmeal**
4 oz. [½ cup] **butter**
1 small **onion**
¼ teaspoon freshly ground black **pepper**
½ teaspoon **ground bay leaves**
¼ teaspoon **kelp powder**
sea salt
1 tablespoon **wheat germ**

Heat the oven to 375°F (Gas Mark 5, 190°C).
Wash the fish well and dry on kitchen paper. Mix the oatmeal and half the butter with a fork. Chop the onion finely and combine it with the oatmeal and butter. Season with the pepper, ground bay leaves and kelp, adding a little more if preferred, and a grinding of sea salt to taste.
Blend together well.
Pack this stuffing into the fish, lay them on a large piece of buttered

aluminium foil. Dot with the rest of the butter and gather the foil loosely together over the top of the fish. Bake for 15-20 minutes or until the fish is cooked through.
Open the foil, sprinkle the fish with wheat germ and crisp under the grill [broiler] before serving.

Creamy shrimp scallops

This delicious hot first course looks very attractive served in scallop shells.
Preparation and cooking time:
40 minutes
S E R V E S 4

1 **shallot, chopped finely**
1 tablespoon **butter**
5 fl. oz. [⅝ cup] **natural yogurt**
2 **egg yolks**
8 oz. cooked **shrimps, shelled**
2 teaspoons chopped **parsley**
sea salt
freshly ground black pepper
1 tablespoon grated **Parmesan cheese**

Heat the oven to 350°F (Gas Mark 4, 180°C).
Cook the chopped shallot in the butter until soft.
Beat the yogurt and egg yolks together. Stir in the shrimps, the softened shallot and parsley. Season to taste.
Pour into scallop shells or greased ramekin dishes and sprinkle with Parmesan cheese. Bake for 25 minutes until set and golden.

Fish fillets, Spanish style

White fish combines well with the rich flavours of green peppers, mushrooms and tomatoes.
Preparation and cooking time:
45 minutes
S E R V E S 4

1½ lb. cod **fillet**
1 medium-sized **onion**
1 garlic **clove**
1 celery **stalk**
½ medium-sized green **pepper**
4 oz. **mushrooms**
8 oz. **tomatoes**
2 tablespoons **butter**
1 tablespoon **corn oil**
3 fl. oz. [⅜ cup] **water**
1 tablespoon **tomato purée**

1 tablespoon white wine
sea salt
freshly ground black pepper
Worcestershire sauce
To garnish:
chopped parsley

Poach the fish gently in lightly salted water for 15-20 minutes or until it is cooked through but still firm. Then drain and keep hot.

Meanwhile, peel and chop the onion, crush the garlic, wash and finely chop the celery and de-seed and chop the green pepper. Wash, dry and chop the mushrooms, skin and chop the tomatoes.
Melt the butter and oil in a heavy pan and fry onion and garlic gently for a few minutes. Add the rest of the vegetables, the water, tomato purée and wine. Simmer for about 20

Quick to cook, flavourful and extremely versatile, fish provides both protein and vitamins.

minutes or until soft and thick, adding a little more water if it reduces too much.
Season the sauce to taste with salt, pepper and Worcestershire sauce. Pour the sauce over the fish. Garnish with plenty of chopped parsley and serve.

cheese

Cheese is one of the most versatile and nourishing foods available. It really does contribute a great deal to a balanced diet. It is full of protein (weight for weight, Cheddar cheese supplies marginally more than best fillet steak), and contains vitamins A, B, B2, and E. The immense variety of dishes, sauces and snacks you can prepare with just a good piece of cheese as a starting point makes it one of the best possible buys. Cheddar or one of the other hard cheeses is best for cooking, and it can be slightly stale. (For grating, the harder it is the better.) For salads, on the other hand, the cheese should be firm and fresh. Creamy fresh-tasting cottage cheese is particularly good in salads. Processed cheese is useful as a store-cupboard standby, but is unsuitable for cooking because it contains extra water and additives. Cheese should be stored in a cool place, covered loosely. It will go hard quickly if it is entirely exposed to air. And if it is tightly covered it is likely to mould. Although cheese often requires months, or years, to ripen to full maturity, once ripe it does deteriorate rapidly. So buy it in fairly small quantities—enough to last just a few days. There are so many uses for cheese that there should be no problem in finishing it off quickly. Below are some quick ideas, but try the recipes, too.

Dips
Make a cold cheese dip with cream cheese or cottage cheese and sour cream combined with a dash of prepared mustard. Serve with raw carrots or other crisp raw vegetables.

Dressing and garnishes
Grated cheese is a good garnish for soups and vegetables. (Brown it under the grill [broiler] if you like.) Crumbled Roquefort or Danish blue cheese mixed with natural yogurt makes a good dressing to serve with salads.

Hot snacks
Add a couple of quick cheese bakes to your repertoire. Slices of ham rolled around cooked chicory, topped with a cheesy sauce and baked in the oven taste delicious. So do green peppers filled with a minced [ground] beef or nut-based stuffing, topped with grated cheese and baked.

Cottage cheese and mushroom quiche

⧗ ⧗

This lunch or supper dish uses eggs and the added protein of cottage cheese. It may be served either with vegetables or a green salad.
Preparation and cooking time:
1¼ hours
S E R V E S   4-6

6 oz. [1½ cups] **flour**
a pinch of sea salt
3 oz. [⅜ cup] **margarine**
water
For the filling:
1 tablespoon chopped onion
2 tablespoons vegetable oil
6-8 mushrooms, sliced
3 eggs
8 oz. cottage cheese
2 oz. cooked ham *or* **boiled bacon, chopped**
2 tablespoons chopped fresh tarragon
1 teaspoon sea salt
a pinch of freshly ground black pepper

Heat the oven to 425°F (Gas Mark 7, 220°C).
Sift together the flour and salt and rub in the margarine. Add just enough water to make a firm dough. Roll out and use it to line a greased 8-inch pie plate.
Fry the onion gently in a little oil until soft but not brown. Add mushrooms and cook until they begin to soften.
Beat the eggs and mix well with the cottage cheese. Add the onion and mushroom with the ham or bacon, tarragon and seasoning.
Pour mixture into the prepared pastry case and bake for 15 minutes. Lower the heat to 350°F (Gas Mark 4, 180°C) and bake for a further 40 to 50 minutes, or until the filling has risen and is firm to the touch.

Cottage cheese and smoked fish cocottes

⧗ ⧗

The fish and cottage cheese flavours complement each other particularly well in this dish.
Preparation and cooking time:
1¼ hours
S E R V E S   4

8 oz. smoked haddock or kipper fillets, fresh or frozen
8 oz. cottage cheese
1 medium-sized onion, chopped and lightly cooked in butter
4 oz. mushrooms, chopped
2 eggs
the juice of 1 lemon
sea salt
freshly ground black pepper
To garnish:
lemon twists
parsley sprigs

Heat the oven to 375°F (Gas Mark 5, 190°C).
Poach smoked fish in a little milk. Skin and flake the fish and mix with the cottage cheese, onion and mushrooms. Beat the eggs and add to mixture. Add lemon juice and season to taste.
Grease 4 cocotte or ramekin dishes and divide the mixture between them. Stand in a baking tin of warm water and bake in the oven for 40 minutes or until set.
Garnish with lemon twists and sprigs of parsley.

Cottage cheese lunch platter

⧗ ☆

This is a good light lunch dish, which could also be served as a first course. Other fresh herbs such as basil and tarragon may be used, but they should always be added cautiously, tasting as you go.
Preparation time:
45 minutes
S E R V E S   4

1 medium-sized cucumber
4 large tomatoes
1 small lettuce
8 oz. cottage cheese
1 tablespoon chopped fresh chives
4 spikes fresh rosemary, chopped
1 teaspoon chopped thyme
1 teaspoon chopped lemon balm
½ teaspoon dried caraway seeds
2 tablespoons sour cream
1 teaspoon sea salt
¼ teaspoon freshly ground black pepper
To garnish:
sprigs of parsley

Peel the cucumber, cut into 8 pieces and remove seeds. Sprinkle well with salt and leave for 30 minutes.
Wash the tomatoes, cut a slice from the tops and scoop out the seeds. Save the slices for garnish.

Wash the lettuce, dry and wrap in a cloth. Crisp in the refrigerator until required.

Turn the cottage cheese into a bowl and mix in the chopped herbs, sour cream and seasonings. Taste and add more salt and pepper if required.

Drain the moisture from the cucumber pieces, and arrange the lettuce leaves on a serving platter. Pack the herby cottage cheese filling into the tomatoes and cucumber pieces and arrange them on the lettuce.

Garnish with sprigs of parsley and slivers from tomato tops.

Pizza with cheese and olives

This pizza, based on an easy yeast dough, makes a complete meal if you serve it with a crisp salad. Alternatively, serve it in small portions as a first course.

Preparation and cooking time:
1 hour 50 minutes
S E R V E S   6-8

For the pizza base:
¼ teaspoon sugar
3 tablespoons tepid water (110°F, 43°C)
½ tablespoon dried yeast
8 oz. wholemeal [2 cups wholewheat] flour
1 teaspoon sea salt
2 eggs
2 oz. [¼ cup] soft butter
For the topping:
1 lb. ripe tomatoes
1 medium-sized onion
1 small garlic clove
1 tablespoon cooking oil
½ teaspoon sea salt
¼ teaspoon black pepper
3 oz. sharp cheese
1 teaspoon chopped fresh marjoram
    or ½ teaspoon dried marjoram
1 teaspoon chopped fresh thyme
    or ½ teaspoon dried thyme
½ teaspoon chopped fresh rosemary
    or ¼ teaspoon dried rosemary
12 black olives
1 tablespoon capers (optional)

Stir the sugar into the water, sprinkle the yeast on top and leave for 10 minutes.

Mix the flour and salt together in a warm bowl. Beat the eggs into the yeast liquid and add to the flour. Work in the butter.

Cover the bowl with a clean cloth and set it in a warm, draught-free place. Leave it for 45 minutes, or until the

dough has risen and doubled in bulk.

Meanwhile, make the topping. Scald the tomatoes in boiling water, skin and chop roughly. Peel and chop the onion. Skin and crush the garlic. Fry the onion and garlic gently in the oil until soft and translucent, then add the tomatoes. Cook to a soft purée, then turn up the heat to reduce. Turn into a bowl to cool and season with salt and pepper.

Heat the oven to 400°F (Gas Mark 6, 200°C).

Flour a baking sheet. Place the risen

Use cottage cheese, a cheap source of protein, either cold in a lunch platter or hot in a quiche.

dough on it and pat into a 9-inch circle. Spread the tomato mixture on top, leaving a half-inch border.

Grate the cheese over the top, sprinkle with the herbs and garnish with the olives and capers.

Leave the pizza for 15 minutes in a warm place to allow the dough to rise again, then bake for 20-25 minutes until browned and cooked through.

yogurt

Yogurt—what it is, and what it can do for you

'Yogurt' is in fact the Bulgarian and Turkish name for fermented milk—but it has many other names. In India it is called *dahi*; in the Balkans, *tarho*; in the Eastern Carpathians, *huslanka*; in Southern Russia and the Caucasus, *kefir* or *kuban*; in Egypt and most of Asia Minor, *leben* or *laban*, in Siberia and Central Asia, *koumiss*.

Yogurt has become popular in Western countries only during recent years, but it has for many centuries been part of the everyday diet of people in Eastern Europe, the Middle and Far East and Africa. Milk—from cows, sheep or goats—was one of the basic foods of many tribes and civilizations and as it does not stay fresh for very long, people experimented to find a way to make sour milk palatable. Fermentation, perhaps using a piece of decaying vegetable or animal matter to trigger off the process, was found to be the answer to the problem. The flavour and consistency of the finished yogurt varied from country to country and tribe to tribe depending on the method and length of fermentation, the type of milk and the kind of feeding stuff used for the animals.

The first scientific investigations into yogurt were made by Metchnikoff in 1907 at the Pasteur Institute in Paris. He was attracted by the idea that people living in Bulgarian villages ate vast quantities of sour milk and were supposed to live for a very long time —100 years or more. He studied the substance, and isolated a strong lactic acid-producing organism. This he named 'long-life bacillus' and it is used in the making of today's yogurt.

How yogurt is made

Yogurt contains all the food value of milk, but it has most of the fat removed and extra protein and vitamins added. Yogurt is commercially prepared from fresh, high-quality milk and is extremely good for you, but homemade yogurt is infinitely preferable. This is not because it is any more nutritious —in fact, it isn't—but it has a flavour and texture that commercially prepared yogurt never has.

Never freeze yogurt, store it in a refrigerator or cold larder and it will keep for two weeks or more quite safely. If it is kept in a warm room its acid content increases rapidly and this gives the yogurt a 'sharper' taste which many people find unpleasant.

Food value

Yogurt is an important source of protein. (See chart p.4). It also has the advantage of being highly digestible—about three times as digestible as milk —which makes it a good food for invalids or anyone feeling fragile.

For slimmers, there is also the advantage of protein without excessive calories. (5 ounces of low-fat unsweetened yogurt would supply about 75 calories whereas two slices of lean beef supply 150 calories.)

Versatility

Yogurt is not only nutritious; it is also, for the imaginative and health-conscious cook, marvellously versatile. It is included in recipes coming from many countries. In India yogurt is eaten with meat and vegetable curries, with sugar, honey, fruit and molasses. In Russia it is added to soups and stews. In Bulgaria and Turkey it is an important ingredient in many delicious dishes.

The consistency and bland flavour of yogurt bring out and subtly add to many other food flavours. It has the versatility of cream, without the fat content.

Yogurt machines

The main problem in making your own yogurt is to keep the milk warm for the 10-16 hours while fermentation takes place. One good way to overcome this difficulty is to use an electric yogurt-making machine with a thermostatically controlled fermentation chamber. These all come with specific instructions but the basic method is simply to place one tablespoon of shop-bought yogurt in the chamber, top up with milk, switch on and leave overnight.

Vitamins

All commercial yogurts supply valuable quantities of the 'B' vitamins, but quantities of vitamins A and D vary from brand to brand. (One very popular brand supplies 603 International Units of vitamin A per 100 grams and 83.3 International Units of vitamin D per 100 grams.)

Blackberry cooler

This is a light and digestible yogurt drink to make when it is too hot to eat a full meal.
Preparation and cooking time:
10 minutes, plus chilling time
S E R V E S 4

8 oz. blackberries
10 fl. oz. [1¼ cups] natural
　yogurt
2 egg yolks
2 tablespoons clear honey, or
　to taste

Stew the blackberries with just enough water to prevent them sticking to the pan, for 4 or 5 minutes, pressing down with a spoon to extract the juice. Rub them through a fine sieve to remove pips. Chill the purée until required.
Combine blackberry purée, yogurt, egg yolks and honey in a blender and blend at full speed for 2 minutes. Then serve.

Homemade natural yogurt

Making yogurt at home is quite simple, but it often has a thin consistency. This method gives a closer curd which is preferable for most desserts.
Preparation time:
30 minutes, plus 12 hours to incubate the yogurt
M A K E S 1 pint [2½ cups]

1 pint [2½ cups] milk
3 tablespoons dried skimmed milk
　powder (not instant granules)
1 tablespoon commercial live
　yogurt

Bring the milk to the boil, lower heat and simmer for 5 minutes. Remove to a bowl and cool to blood heat. (If the milk is too warm, the yogurt will separate.) The bowl may be placed in iced water to speed up cooling.
Sprinkle the skimmed milk powder on to the milk and mix it in with a fork. Stir in the live yogurt.
Turn the mixture into a wide-mouthed vacuum jar which has been rinsed out with warm water, close and leave for 12 hours or overnight. Turn out and refrigerate until needed.

Homemade Yogurt (top) is used to make a Yogurt and Orange Whip (below).

Lemon consommé with yogurt

This is a light, refreshing cold soup with a sharp, tangy taste.
Preparation and cooking time:
10 minutes, plus setting time
SERVES 4

16 fl. oz. [2 cups] consommé (canned)
2 teaspoonfuls dry sherry
the juice and grated zest of ½ lemon
10 fl. oz. [1¼ cups] natural yogurt
3 sprigs fresh or 2 sprigs dried
tarragon, if available

Warm together the consommé, sherry and lemon juice. Pour into individual soup bowls and chill. *Combine* the grated lemon zest, yogurt and tarragon. When the consommé has set, and just before serving, remove the sprigs of tarragon from yogurt, then spoon it on to consommé.

Oriental dressing

This goes well with any salad which combines fruit and vegetables. It is also good served with cold meats.
Preparation time:
5 minutes, plus chilling time
MAKES 5 fluid ounces

5 fl. oz. [⅝ cup] natural yogurt
1 teaspoon curry powder
½ teaspoon finely grated lemon zest
2 teaspoons lemon juice
½ teaspoon chopped mixed herbs
¼ teaspoon sea salt

Combine all the ingredients and chill well before serving.

Piquant dressing

This has a tangy flavour which is marvellous with a salad.
Preparation time: *5 minutes*
MAKES 5 fluid ounces

5 fl. oz. [⅝ cup] natural yogurt
1 tablespoon chopped chives
¼ teaspoon dry mustard
¼ teaspoon garlic salt
1 teaspoon lemon juice
sea salt
freshly ground black pepper

Combine all the ingredients and serve immediately.

Watercress dressing

Watercress has a strong, pungent flavour and is rich in iron and vitamin E. This dressing is good with roast meats, especially beef.
Preparation time:
5 minutes
MAKES 5 fluid ounces

a small bunch watercress
5 fl. oz. [⅝ cup] natural yogurt
½ teaspoon lemon juice
sea salt
freshly ground black pepper

Remove the coarse stalks from the watercress. Chop the rest finely. Mix in the yogurt and lemon juice and season to taste.

Yogurt and orange whip

This refreshing and tangy summer dessert can be made with any fruit. But you do need a blender to make it successfully.
Preparation time:
15 minutes, plus 2 hours chilling time
SERVES 4

8 medium-sized oranges
2 tablespoons honey
1 pint [2½ cups] yogurt
4 tablespoons chopped walnuts,
almonds or hazelnuts

Peel the oranges, removing as much of the white pith as possible. Reserve about 2 teaspoons of the orange rind and chop it finely. Set aside.
Chop the orange flesh into small pieces with a serrated-edge knife, and place them in a blender. Add the honey and yogurt and blend at high speed for about 20 seconds, or until the ingredients are well combined.
Pour the orange mixture into four individual glass serving dishes. Place them in the refrigerator and chill for at least 2 hours.
Just before serving, sprinkle the tops with the nuts and reserved orange rind.

vegetables

Vegetables deserve to be cooked with as much care and attention as meat. They can stand alone very successfully too. The European idea of serving the vegetable course separately from the meat is a good one. After a cooked meat dish, a clean-tasting dish of short-cooked green vegetables or a vegetable salad provides a change of texture and some work for digestive juices. (And it adds roughage to the meal, especially if the vegetables are crunchy and chewy.)
Food values in vegetables vary according to the way they are stored before cooking, and how you cook them. Vitamin C is volatile. It dissolves in water and evaporates with moisture if the vegetables are exposed to the air. Vitamin A, which is found in things like carrots, loses potency through heat. So cook vegetables quickly in very little water, and serve them still crunchy. There are three substantial vegetable dishes in this section: a curry, a casserole and a couscous. There is also a bean salad. And this raises the subject of which vegetables are suitable for salads. Lettuce, tomatoes and cucumbers may be the favourites but shredded raw cabbage, cold cooked potatoes, spinach leaves, grated carrot, grated turnip and cauliflower are just as suitable. (The dressing given for the Bean Salad is also delicious used with all the vegetables above.)

Aubergine [Eggplant] casserole

The aubergine [eggplant] is an exotic vegetable that is also very adaptable. This recipe is Middle Eastern in origin but its marvellous flavour will appeal to everyone. Serve the casserole hot or cold.
Preparation and cooking time:
2½ hours
SERVES 4

10 oz. dried chick-peas, soaked
overnight and drained or 14 oz.
canned chick-peas, drained
1½ pints [3¾ cups] water
2 medium-sized aubergines
[eggplants]
1½ teaspoons sea salt

7 fl. oz. [⅞ cup] olive oil
4 small courgettes [zucchini]
    washed, trimmed and sliced into
    ¼-inch slices
2 medium-sized onions, sliced
2 garlic cloves, crushed
8 oz. canned peeled tomatoes,
    drained and chopped with liquid
    reserved
½ teaspoon cayenne pepper
1 teaspoon ground cumin

If you are using dried chick-peas,
put them into a large saucepan and
pour in the water. Place the pan
over moderately high heat and bring
the water to the boil. Reduce the
heat to low, partially cover the pan
and cook for 45 minutes, or until the
peas are just tender. Remove the pan
from the heat and drain the chick-
peas in a colander. Set aside. (If
you are using canned chick-peas, the
above step can be omitted.)
Meanwhile, peel the aubergines
[eggplants] and dice the flesh.
Place the pieces in a colander and
sprinkle them with 1 teaspoon of
the salt. Leave them for 30 minutes,
then drain on kitchen paper towels.
Heat 4 fluid ounces [½ cup] of the
oil in a large frying pan over
moderate heat. When the oil is hot,
add the chopped aubergine [eggplant]
and cook, stirring occasionally, for
10 minutes, or until the pieces are
evenly browned on all sides.
Transfer the aubergine [eggplant]
and any cooking liquid to a large
mixing bowl.
Heat the oven to 350°F (Gas Mark 4,
180°C).
Heat the remaining oil in the frying
pan, over moderate heat. When the
oil is hot, add the courgette
[zucchini] slices to the pan. Cook
them, stirring occasionally, for 8 to
10 minutes, or until they are evenly
browned. With a slotted spoon,
transfer the courgette [zucchini]
slices to the mixing bowl with the
aubergines [eggplants]. Set aside.
Add the onions and garlic to the pan
and cook them, stirring occasionally,
for 5-7 minutes, or until the
onions are soft and translucent but
not brown. Add the tomatoes, the
remaining salt, the cayenne and cumin
to the pan and stir well to mix.
Cook the tomato mixture for 3
minutes, then remove the pan from
the heat and stir the mixture into the
aubergine [eggplant] mixture. Stir in
the chick-peas and the reserved
tomato juice.
Transfer the mixture to a deep
ovenproof casserole. Place it

in the centre of the oven and bake
for 1 hour, or until all of the
vegetables are tender. Serve at once.
(If you want to serve the casserole
cold, allow it to cool to room
temperature, then place it in the
refrigerator to chill for at least
2 hours.)

Bean salad

⬚

Serve this with cold meat or as part
of a summer buffet meal.
Preparation and cooking time:
30 minutes
S E R V E S 2-4

1 lb. green beans
2 tablespoons olive *or* sunflower
    oil
the juice of 1 lemon
1 medium-sized onion
1 clove garlic (optional)
1 teaspoon chopped parsley
1 teaspoon chopped savory
sea salt
freshly ground black pepper
a few lettuce leaves
To garnish:
1 egg, hard-boiled and chopped

Cook the beans in a little boiling
salted water until tender, drain and
cool.
Mix the oil and lemon juice. Slice the
onion finely and slice or crush
garlic and mix into the dressing,
adding the herbs and seasoning. Pour
dressing over the beans.
Pile the beans on to the lettuce
leaves and serve garnished with the
egg.

Curry creole

⬚

This spicy yet refreshing mixture
of fruit and vegetables makes a
delightful summer supper dish.
Serve it with boiled rice and a
tossed green salad.
Preparation and cooking time:
1 hour
S E R V E S 4

4 oz. [½ cup] butter or margarine
2 medium-sized onions, thinly
    sliced
1 garlic clove, crushed
1 green chilli, de-seeded and
    chopped
4 small courgettes [zucchini],
    trimmed, washed and cut into
    ¼-inch slices

1 large red pepper, de-seeded and
    sliced
1½ lb. sweet potato, peeled and
    diced into 1-inch cubes
3 tomatoes, blanched, peeled,
    seeded and chopped
2 medium-sized bananas, sliced
2 oz. canned pineapple chunks,
    drained
1 teaspoon ground coriander
½ teaspoon ground cardamom
½ teaspoon ground fenugreek
½ teaspoon turmeric
¼ teaspoon hot chilli powder
3 tablespoons water
10 fl. oz. [1¼ cups] vegetable
    stock
1-inch slice creamed coconut

Melt the butter or margarine in a
large saucepan over moderate heat.
When the foam subsides, add the
onions, garlic, chilli, courgettes
[zucchini], red pepper and sweet
potato. Cook them, stirring
occasionally, for 10 minutes.
Add the tomatoes, bananas and
pineapple chunks and cook, stirring
frequently, for 3 minutes.
Combine the coriander, cardamom,
fenugreek, turmeric and chilli powder
with the water in a small bowl to
make a smooth paste.
Stir the spice mixture into the fruit
and vegetable mixture, then pour in
the vegetable stock. Increase the
heat to high and bring the stock to
the boil. Reduce the heat to low,
cover the pan and simmer for 15
minutes, or until the vegetables are
cooked.
Stir in the creamed coconut, mixing
until it dissolves and the liquid
thickens. Simmer for a further 2
minutes.
Remove the pan from the heat and
turn the curry into a warmed serving
dish. Serve immediately.

Jerusalem artichokes
flavoured with
rosemary

⬚

Jerusalem artichokes should never be
overcooked, and this recipe
tastes best if the vegetables
retain a crunchy texture.
Preparation and cooking time:
30 minutes
S E R V E S 4

1½ lb. Jerusalem artichokes
1 tablespoon flour
2 tablespoons vinegar
water

sea salt
3 tablespoons butter
2 sprigs fresh rosemary, chopped
    or 1 sprig dried rosemary

Scrub the artichokes carefully and peel them very thinly. Reserve until cooking time in water to which 1 tablespoon flour and 2 tablespoonfuls vinegar have been added. (This prevents discolouration.)
When ready to cook, cut the artichokes in thick slices and place in a saucepan with just enough water to cover and a little salt. Boil until soft but not mushy and then strain.
Melt the butter in a saucepan, add the artichokes and rosemary, and shake the pan to prevent sticking.
Warm the artichokes through, and serve completely covered with the butter and rosemary mixture.

Moroccan vegetable couscous

◻ ◻ ◻

Serve this exotic dish with a light salad, crusty brown bread and lots of cool beer or white wine.
If you do not have a couscoussier, you can construct a temporary one by placing a colander lined with cheesecloth on top of a saucepan and sealing the space between the colander and the rim of the pan with a twisted, damp cloth.
Preparation and cooking time:
3¼ hours
SERVES 6

1 lb. couscous
18 fl. oz. [2¼ cups] lukewarm
    salted water
6 medium-sized courgettes
    [zucchini], trimmed, washed and
    sliced in half crosswise, then
    sliced in half lengthways
2 large green peppers, cored,
    de-seeded and sliced
2 large onions, quartered
3 medium-sized potatoes, scrubbed
    and sliced
1 small turnip, peeled and sliced
4 large carrots, scraped and
    quartered
3 pints [7½ cups] cold water
3 oz. [⅜ cup] butter *or* margarine,
    melted
1 lb. canned chick-peas, drained
4 oz. [⅔ cup] seedless raisins
2 oz. [⅓ cup] blanched almonds
1 lb. tomatoes, quartered
3 garlic cloves, crushed
3 green chillis, seeds removed and
finely chopped
2 teaspoons sea salt
1 teaspoon freshly ground black
    pepper
½ teaspoon cayenne pepper
2 teaspoons ground cumin
2 teaspoons paprika
½ teaspoon ground saffron, dissolved
    in 1 teaspoon hot water
3 teaspoons turmeric
2 teaspoons ground coriander

Put the couscous grains into a large mixing bowl. Pour over 16 fluid ounces [2 cups] of the lukewarm water. Leave the couscous to soak for 1 hour, or until it swells slightly. Drain the grains in a fine strainer and set them aside.
Meanwhile, put the courgettes [zucchini], green peppers, onions, potatoes, turnip and carrots into the bottom half of the couscoussier. Pour in 2 pints [5 cups] of the cold water and bring the water to the boil over moderately high heat. Reduce the heat to low, cover the pan and simmer the vegetables for 30 minutes.
Fit the top half, or steamer, on to the couscoussier and pour the couscous grains into the steamer. Cover the pan and cook the mixture for 40 minutes.
Remove the top half, or steamer, from the couscoussier and transfer the couscous grains to a large mixing bowl. Pour on the melted butter or margarine and remaining lukewarm salted water. Leave the mixture to soak for 15 minutes.
Meanwhile, add the chick-peas, raisins, almonds and tomatoes to the bottom half of the couscoussier and pour in the remaining 1 pint [2½ cups] of cold water. Stir in the garlic, chillis, salt, pepper and spices. Bring the liquid to the boil over moderately high heat. Reduce the heat to low and simmer the mixture for 15 minutes.
Stir the couscous grains, breaking up any lumps that have formed and return the couscous to the top part, or steamer, of the couscoussier. Fit this attachment to the couscoussier again, cover and cook the mixture for a further 20 minutes.
Remove the couscoussier from the heat and take off the top half. Arrange the vegetable mixture in a large, deep serving dish and spoon on some of the cooking liquid. Reserve about 4 fluid ounces [½ cup] of the cooking liquid and discard the rest.
Put the couscous grains into a
second serving dish and pour over the reserved cooking liquid. Serve at once.

Sweet and sour carrots

◻

This is a very different way to prepare a homely but delicious vegetable. Serve it as an accompaniment to risottos or omelettes.
Preparation and cooking time:
40 minutes
SERVES 4

1 lb. carrots, scraped and sliced
1½ pints [3¾ cups] water
½ teaspoon salt
1½ oz. [3 tablespoons] butter or
    margarine
2 tablespoons flour
1 tablespoon honey
1 tablespoon wine vinegar
1 tablespoon chopped fresh parsley

Put the carrots into a large saucepan. Pour in the water and add the salt. Place the pan over moderately high heat and bring the water to the boil. Reduce the heat to moderate and cook the carrots for 10 to 15 minutes, or until they are tender. Drain the carrots and reserve 12 fluid ounces [1½ cups] of the cooking liquid.
Melt the butter or margarine over moderate heat in a medium-sized saucepan. Remove the pan from the heat and, with a wooden spoon, stir in the flour to make a smooth paste. Gradually add the reserved cooking liquid, stirring constantly.
Return the pan to the heat and cook the sauce stirring constantly, for 3 to 4 minutes, or until it is smooth and fairly thick. Stir in the honey and vinegar.
Add the carrots to the pan and continue to cook for 2 minutes, basting the carrots well with the sauce.
Turn the carrots and sauce into a warmed serving dish. Sprinkle the parsley over the carrots and serve.

Curry Creole (recipe page 33) is a delicious blend of fruit and vegetables that makes a meal on its own.

raw foods

Food is usually cooked to make it easier to chew and digest, and more appetizing to look at. But some foods taste and look just as good uncooked, particularly fruits and vegetables. And by serving green vegetables raw, much of the valuable vitamin C is preserved —instead of being washed away with the vegetable water. Many vegetables are delicious chopped and served in salad form: carrots, cucumber, cauliflower, mushrooms and cabbage all lend themselves well to this.

Combine raw fruits and vegetables to make interesting salads. Herbs, lemon juice and sometimes natural yogurt can also be added to improve the flavour. And nuts and raisins will add not only extra food value but also variety of taste and texture.

Health drinks

Fruit juices and vegetable drinks can supply valuable vitamins and variety, to your diet. A blender is, therefore, a good investment if you're slimming. But if you do not have a blender, you can squeeze fruits, or simmer vegetables in a little water, then press them through a sieve and allow to cool.

Experiment with unusual herbs and vegetables for juices; they can be very good for you. Parsley juice, for example, is a rich source of vitamins A and C, and one of the few plants in which both these vitamins are present. Watercress juice supplies these vitamins too, plus iron and calcium. Cabbage juice or cabbage water is a particularly good base for a vegetable juice cocktail, and supplies vitamins A and C, calcium and iron. But the most nutritious of all is carrot juice. The juice of just four ounces of carrots supplies about half a day's requirements of Vitamin A, plus calcium, iodine, potassium, sulphur and sodium.

All fruit and vegetable juices taste better chilled. But drink them immediately they are brought into room temperature otherwise microscopic fungi will begin the work of fermentation, and impair the flavour.

Leek, cole slaw and peppery salads all look as good as they taste.

Beansprout salad
Mix drained, canned beansprouts with sliced mushrooms, firm tomato wedges, and chopped celery. Toss in lemon juice.

Brussels sprout salad
Mix shredded young sprouts with grated carrots, chopped celery, cauliflower sprigs, and chopped chives.

Celery salad
Mix shredded celery with shredded raw red or white cabbage, chopped onions, diced unpeeled eating apple and mustard and cress. Toss in a little yogurt mixed with horseradish for added piquancy.

Cole slaw salad
Mix shredded white cabbage with an equal quantity of shredded carrot, a diced apple and some natural, unsweetened yogurt. Add a few chives and a squeeze of lemon juice.

Crispy salad
Combine finely-shredded white cabbage, a few sprigs of cauliflower, chopped celery, sliced button mushrooms and a few almonds with a dressing of unsweetened tomato juice, tarragon vinegar and soy sauce. Leave to stand in a cool place, then cover with a few sliced mushrooms and capers and serve.

Leek salad
Slice some well-washed leeks finely and break them into rings. Mix with chopped chives and parsley and toss in lemon juice.

Mushroom and onion salad
Slice mushrooms and combine with grated onion and a little mild mustard. Add a few chopped tomatoes and garnish with cayenne pepper.

Peppery salad
Make a dressing with tomato juice, Worcestershire sauce and wine vinegar. Slice red, yellow or green peppers and a few mushrooms. Toss in the dressing and garnish with lettuce leaves.

Turnip salad
Peel and slice a small turnip and mix with shredded white cabbage, carrots, watercress, and sliced tomatoes.

Watercress and carrot salad
Mix chopped young carrots with watercress, chives, diced cucumber and a little chopped onion.

Beetroot [Beet] and parsley salad
☆ ◻

Beetroot [beets] can be very dull when served only in sharp malt vinegar. A sweeter dressing brings out their flavour, especially when combined with parsley and grated orange zest.
Preparation time: *10 minutes*
SERVES 4

1 lb. cooked beetroot [beets]
2 teaspoons grated orange zest
2 tablespoons chopped parsley
For the dressing:
4 fl. oz. [½ cup] olive or corn oil
2 tablespoons wine vinegar or lemon juice
1 teaspoon honey
sea salt
freshly ground black pepper

Peel and dice the beetroot [beets]. *Combine* the ingredients for the dressing and mix well. Toss the beetroot [beets] in the dressing and scatter parsley and grated orange zest over it before serving.

Crunchy winter salad
☆ ◻

There is no need to cut down on health-giving salads in the winter. This one has a delicious blend of flavours and an agreeable crunchy texture. The proportions of the ingredients may be altered according to availability.
Preparation time: *15 minutes*
SERVES 4

½ medium-sized firm white cabbage
1 small bulb fennel
2 medium carrots
1 eating apple
¼ medium-sized green pepper
2 tablespoons cashew nuts
2 tablespoons raisins
6-8 sprigs parsley
1 medium onion (optional)
For the dressing:
4 fl. oz. [½ cup] olive or corn oil
2 tablespoons wine vinegar
1 teaspoon clear honey
sea salt
freshly ground black pepper

Remove outer leaves from the cabbage. Trim the fennel. Scrape the carrots, peel, quarter and core the apple. Wash, core and de-seed the pepper. *Shred* the cabbage finely with a sharp knife, chop the fennel, apple and pepper. Grate carrots and nuts.

Mix all dressing ingredients, beat together and season to taste. Toss the shredded vegetables in the dressing, mix with nuts and raisins and place in salad bowl.
Wash and dry the parsley, chop and scatter over the salad before serving. Top with the onion, cut into rings.

Mushroom and cucumber salad

This unusual and flavoursome salad can be made at any time of the year.
Preparation time: *15 minutes*
SERVES 4

1 small cucumber
4 oz. mushrooms
1 medium-sized onion
3 slices stale wholemeal
  [wholewheat] bread
vegetable oil for frying
For the dressing:
4 fl. oz. [$\frac{1}{2}$ cup] olive or corn oil
2 tablespoons wine vinegar
sea salt
freshly ground black pepper
To garnish:
lettuce leaves

Peel and dice the cucumber. Wash, dry and slice the mushrooms. Peel the onion and cut into fine rings.
Beat together all the ingredients for the dressing.
Trim the crusts from the bread, cut into $\frac{1}{2}$-inch cubes and fry in a little hot oil until crisp. Drain well.
Just before serving, toss the vegetables and croûtons well in the dressing and arrange on a bed of lettuce leaves.

Turkish salad

This tastes delicious with beef stew.
Preparation time: *45 minutes*
SERVES 4-6

1 cucumber
2-3 garlic cloves
15 fl. oz. [2 cups] natural yogurt
sea salt
freshly ground black pepper
2 tablespoons chopped fresh mint

Slice or dice the cucumber, sprinkle it with salt and leave for 30 minutes.
Crush the garlic into a bowl, mix in the yogurt and season to taste. Add the mint. Strain off the cucumber and add it to the yogurt mixture.

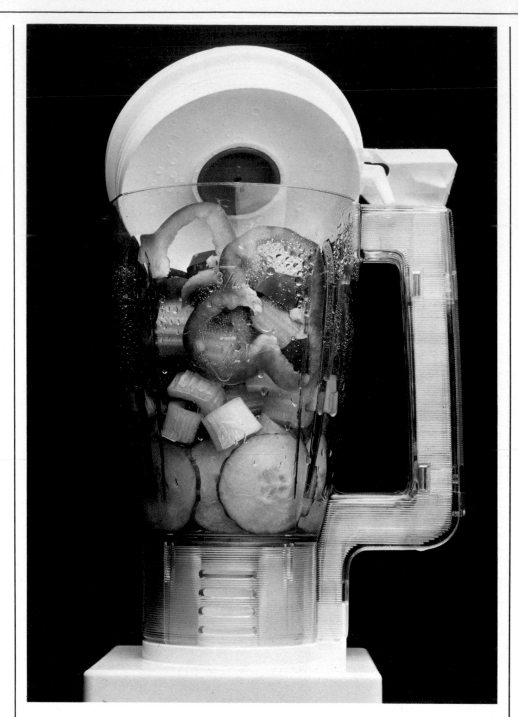

Celery, cucumber and green pepper combine for a health-giving drink.

Fruit juices

1. Equal parts strawberry and pineapple juice.
2. 1 cup apple juice, 1 cup blackberry juice and a teaspoon of honey.
3. 1 cup orange juice, 1 tablespoon cucumber juice, 1 tablespoon lemon juice.
4. 1 cup melon juice, 1 tablespoon orange juice and a dash of lemon juice. Mint and orange slices for garnish.
5. 1 cup apple juice, 1 tablespoon blackcurrant juice and 1 tablespoon natural, unsweetened yogurt.
6. 1 cup orange juice, 1 tablespoon peach juice, 1 teaspoon lime juice.

Vegetable juices

1. 1 cup tomato juice, 1 tablespoon lemon juice, and a dash of Worcestershire sauce.
2. Equal parts cabbage, carrot and parsley juice. Cucumber slices and paprika pepper as garnish.
3. 1 cup celery juice, 1 tablespoon parsley juice, 1 tablespoon carrot juice, chopped chives for garnish.
4. 5 fl. oz. [$\frac{5}{8}$ cup] natural, unsweetened yogurt, 4 fl. oz. [$\frac{1}{2}$ cup] tomato juice, and a squeeze of lemon juice.
5. Equal parts juice of celery, cucumber, and green pepper plus a teaspoonful of lemon juice.
6. 1 cup carrot juice, 1 tablespoon cabbage juice and 1 tablespoon turnip juice.

nuts for everybody

Nuts are not just for vegetarians. They provide an interesting addition to any diet and are also a valuable source of protein. To vary your menus, include a nut-based dish occasionally as an alternative to meat, fish, eggs or cheese. Remember, too, that a small packet of peanuts makes a nutritious protein-packed lunch-time snack when it is impossible to have a proper meal. Add nuts to fruit or salad vegetables and you get the bonus of vitamins B and C as well as protein. And if you have a glass of fresh milk as well you get a well-balanced meal without the trouble of cooking.

Brazil nuts provide almost as much protein gram for gram as roast chicken, and more than pork sausages or luncheon meat. So a Nut Bake (recipe over) could be better value for a summer lunch than sliced luncheon meat and salad. Health-food shops have a good choice of nuts—ground, mixed or whole. Try these recipes, then experiment with different tastes and different mixtures. Nut cookery is fun, and the results are delicious!

Do not leave nut cookery to vegetarians. Nut Rolls (recipe on next page) taste delicious and would make a change from a main meat dish.

Foule Sudani

This nourishing peanut soup from the Sudan is rich in protein and vitamins.
Preparation and cooking time:
30 minutes
S E R V E S 4

1 oz. **salted peanuts**
3 oz. **unsalted peanuts**
2 tablespoons **ground nut oil**
2 **medium-sized onions, peeled and chopped**
½ **chicken stock cube, dissolved in 1½ pints [3¾ cups] hot water**
or 1½ **pints [3¾ cups] home-made stock**
freshly ground black pepper
salt

Grind the peanuts in a coffee mill or blender, (a little at a time, otherwise the mill clogs up).
Heat the oil in a large heavy-bottomed pan over moderate heat. Fry the onions in the oil until golden brown.
Add the stock to the pan with the ground peanuts, bring to the boil, then reduce the heat and simmer for 10 minutes.
Remove the pan from the heat. Transfer the contents of the pan to a blender or food mill and blend thoroughly, then re-heat.
Season with pepper and salt to taste. (If you use a stock cube, this soup does not normally need extra salt.)

Hazelnut pear salad

This aromatic salad with its unusual combination of flavours makes a filling luncheon dish.
Preparation time:
15 minutes
S E R V E S 4

4 **large pears**
2 teaspoons **lemon juice**
8 oz. **cottage cheese**
4 oz. **[⅔ cup] hazelnuts, coarsely chopped**
2 teaspoons **finely chopped sweet cicely (optional)**
1 teaspoon **finely chopped lemon balm (optional)**
6 **lettuce leaves**

Peel the pears, halve them and remove the cores. Chop the flesh into a medium-sized mixing bowl. Sprinkle the lemon juice over the pears.

Stir in the cottage cheese and hazelnuts, with the sweet cicely and lemon balm if you are using them.
Arrange the lettuce leaves on a shallow serving dish. Pile the pear mixture in the centre and serve.

Nut bake

This unusual savoury is suitable for a main course or supper dish. Serve it accompanied by green vegetables or a salad and wholemeal [wholewheat] bread. Any nuts except peanuts can be used.

Preparation and cooking time:
1 hour
S E R V E S 4

8 oz. **[1½ cups] grated nuts**
8 oz. **tomatoes, skinned and sliced**
1 **small onion, finely chopped**
2 **eggs, beaten**
sea salt
1 teaspoon **mixed chopped thyme and marjoram, fresh or dried**

Heat the oven to 400°F (Gas Mark 6, 205°C).
Mix together the nuts, tomatoes and onions. Add the eggs, stir well, then add the salt and herbs.
Grease an ovenproof dish, put in the nut mixture, and bake in the oven for 30-40 minutes until well-risen and golden on the top.

Nut rolls

This tasty dish can be eaten hot or cold and is very good for a picnic or snack lunch. Any type of nuts except peanuts can be used.
Preparation and cooking time:
40 minutes
S E R V E S 4

2 oz. **[4 tablespoons] butter or lard**
2 oz. **wholemeal [½ cup wholewheat] flour**
1 pint **[2½ cups] stock or water**
sea salt
¼ teaspoon **chopped marjoram**
¼ teaspoon **chopped thyme**
1 teaspoon **yeast extract**
4 oz. **wholemeal [2 cups wholewheat] breadcrumbs**
2 oz. **[⅓ cup] nuts, grated**
1 **egg**
2 tablespoons **milk**

Melt the fat in a saucepan over moderate heat. Add the flour and cook gently for 2 minutes, stirring continuously. Add the stock, salt, herbs and yeast extract, mix well and cook for 5 minutes stirring all the time.
Take the pan off the heat, add 3 ounces [1½ cups] of the breadcrumbs and all the nuts. Mix well, leave to cool and then form into sausage-shaped rolls.
Beat together the egg and the milk. Dip the nut rolls into this mixture, and then cover them with the remaining breadcrumbs.
Fry in deep fat for about 10 minutes or until golden brown. Drain on absorbent kitchen paper.

rice

It is difficult to obtain an ample supply of vitamin B2 (riboflavin) in the average Western diet. The usual recommended daily requirement for tip-top health is one to three milligrams, but many nutritionists feel that about four to five milligrams would be a good level. An average portion of liver, or eight small glasses of milk, would supply this required amount but few people eat liver regularly or drink much milk in one day.

It is, therefore, wise to substitute vitamin B rich foods for other foods whenever practical. And about 1 cup of brown rice can add .02 milligrams of vitamin B2, plus the other valuable members of the B family. It is also a versatile accompaniment to many other foods and delicious in its own right. (White, polished rice has the brown husk and germ removed. It supplies very little vitamin B and less vitamin E.) Some recipes are given below, but remember that the rice can be enjoyed just on its own. The nutty taste is far more interesting than that of plain boiled white rice. Use it instead of potatoes, with cold salads or mixed with chopped vegetables and herbs.

Brown rice does, however, take longer to cook. One method is as follows: rinse the rice under the tap in a wire strainer, bring three cups water to boiling point in a large saucepan, add the cup of rice and boil for 5 minutes. Turn down the heat and simmer for 20 minutes. Turn off the heat, add seasoning and leave the rice to stand for about one hour until the remaining water is absorbed. Warm through just before serving.

Avocado rice salad

Unpolished rice is delicious in salads. This one may be used on its own as a first course, or as an accompaniment to cold meats.
Preparation time:
40 minutes
S E R V E S 4

1 small lettuce
2 oz. [⅓ cup] **long-grain unpolished rice**

1 ripe avocado pear
1 lemon
1 small onion
3-inch piece of cucumber
½ green pepper
2 ripe tomatoes, sliced
For the dressing:
4 fl. oz. [½ cup] olive or corn oil
2 tablespoons wine vinegar
½ teaspoon clear honey
sea salt
freshly ground black pepper

Wash the lettuce, pat dry and crisp in the refrigerator.
Cook the rice in boiling, salted water until just tender but not mushy. Strain in a sieve and rinse well under cold running water. Drain and dry.
Halve the avocado pear, scoop out the flesh and dice. Cut the lemon in half and squeeze the juice from one half. Toss the avocado flesh in the lemon juice. Peel and dice the onion and cucumber. De-seed and chop the pepper.
Combine the ingredients for the dressing and beat well. Toss the vegetables and rice in the dressing, arrange on lettuce leaves in a salad bowl or on small dishes. Top with sliced tomato and the remaining half lemon, sliced.

Brazilian rice

This Brazilian method of cooking rice is both simple and tasty.
Preparation and cooking time:
45 minutes
S E R V E S 4

4 tablespoons olive oil
1 large onion, thinly sliced
12 oz. [2 cups] long-grain brown rice, washed, soaked in cold water for 30 minutes and drained
2 tomatoes, blanched, peeled and chopped
1 teaspoon sea salt
1¼ pints [3 cups] boiling water

Heat the oil over moderate heat in a large saucepan. Add the onion and fry it, stirring occasionally, for 5 to 7

minutes, or until it is soft and translucent but not brown. Add the rice and fry for 5 minutes, stirring constantly.
Stir in the tomatoes and salt. Cook for 2 minutes and then pour in the boiling water.
Reduce the heat to low, cover the pan and simmer for 15 to 20 minutes, or until the rice is tender and all the liquid has been absorbed.
Turn the rice into a warmed serving dish and serve immediately.

Chicken liver pilaff

This nutritious main course can be cooked in advance and reheated. Serve it with a green salad.
Preparation and cooking time:
50 minutes
S E R V E S 4

6 oz. [1 cup] **brown rice**
1 pint [2½ cups] water
1½ teaspoons salt
3 tablespoons vegetable oil
1 medium-sized onion, chopped
3 celery stalks, chopped
4 oz. mushrooms, sliced
8 oz. chicken liver, cut in half
½ teaspoon basil
a pinch of nutmeg
½ teaspoon wholemeal [wholewheat] flour
1 tablespoon yeast extract
To garnish:
parsley, chopped

Put the rice, water, 1 teaspoon of salt and 1 tablespoon of the oil into a large saucepan. Bring to the boil then reduce heat and simmer for 45 minutes or until the rice is tender and all the liquid absorbed.
Heat the remaining oil in a large frying pan and sauté the onions, celery, mushrooms and livers in it for 5-7 minutes or until the vegetables and liver are tender. Add the rest of the seasonings, flour and yeast extract. Cook for 1 minute stirring continuously. Add the cooked rice and heat through thoroughly.
Garnish with chopped parsley and serve.

Rice and salmon or tuna salad

This salad is delicious served with a yogurt dressing (see page 32) and wholemeal [wholewheat] bread. The ingredients and proportions can be slightly modified.
Preparation and cooking time:
$1\frac{1}{2}$ hours
SERVES 4

1 tablespoon vegetable oil
6 oz. [1 cup] **brown rice**
1 small onion finely chopped
1 pint [$2\frac{1}{2}$ cups] **water**
1 teaspoon sea salt
8 oz. canned salmon or tuna fish
1 crisp eating apple (tossed in lemon juice to prevent discoloration)
2 medium-sized carrots, grated coarsely
2 oz. [$\frac{1}{2}$ cup] **cabbage, shredded**
2 oz. [$\frac{1}{2}$ cup] **walnuts, coarsely chopped**
To garnish:
1 bunch watercress
4 medium-sized tomatoes, sliced

Heat the oil in a pan and sauté the rice and onion in it for 2 minutes. Add the water and the salt, bring to the boil and simmer, with the lid on the pan, for about 45 minutes or until the rice and onion are tender and the water is absorbed. Set on one side and leave to cool.
Drain the oil from the fish, and flake the flesh.
Mix the rice together with the prepared vegetables. Add the flaked fish and mix well using a kitchen fork to help separate the ingredients.
Heap on to a salad dish, garnish with watercress and tomato slices, and serve.

Rice with chicken and cherries

An exotic and unusual combination of tastes, Chicken and Cherries is an adaptation of an Iranian dish.
Preparation and cooking time:
$1\frac{1}{2}$ hours
SERVES 4

1 x 3 lb. chicken, cut into 8 serving pieces
2 teaspoons sea salt
1 teaspoon finely ground black pepper
4 tablespoons olive oil
2 medium-sized onions, finely sliced
3 fl. oz. [$\frac{3}{8}$ cup] **chicken stock**
$1\frac{1}{2}$ lb. fresh black Morello cherries, stoned or 2 lb. canned Morello cherries, drained and stoned
2 oz. [$\frac{1}{4}$ cup] **sugar**
2 tablespoons water
12 oz. [2 cups] **long-grain rice, washed and drained**
4 oz. [$\frac{1}{2}$ cup] **butter, melted**
$\frac{1}{2}$ teaspoon crushed saffron threads, dissolved in 1 tablespoon hot water

On a chopping board, sprinkle the chicken pieces with the salt and pepper and set aside.
In a large frying-pan heat the oil over moderate heat. When it is hot, add the chicken pieces, a few at a time. Cook them for 5 to 7 minutes on each side or until they are evenly and thoroughly browned.
When the chicken is browned, transfer it to a heated plate. Add the onions to the oil remaining in the frying-pan and fry them for 6 minutes, or until they begin to brown slightly.
Return the chicken pieces to the frying-pan, pour in the chicken stock and bring the mixture to the boil. Reduce the heat to low, cover the pan and cook the chicken for 30 minutes, or until it is tender when pierced with a fork.
While the chicken is simmering, combine the cherries, sugar and water together in a medium-sized saucepan over low heat. Stirring frequently, simmer uncovered for 5 minutes or until the sugar has dissolved and most of the cherry liquid has evaporated. Remove from heat and set aside.
In a large saucepan, bring $2\frac{1}{2}$ pints [$3\frac{3}{4}$ cups] of water to the boil over moderate heat. Add the rice and boil for 5 minutes. Remove the pan from the heat and drain the rice through a strainer. Set aside.
Transfer the chicken pieces to a plate, reserving about 2 tablespoons of the cooking liquid and the browned onion slices.
Put the reserved cooking liquid and half melted butter into a large flame-proof casserole and mix well. Place half of the rice on the bottom of the casserole, spreading it out evenly, and cook over moderate heat for 8 minutes. Remove the casserole from the heat. Add the chicken pieces, onions and about half of the cherries.
Arrange the remainder of the rice on top of the mixture. Pour in the remaining cherries with their cooking liquid, cover the casserole and simmer over very low heat for 15 minutes or until the rice is tender.
Remove about 4 ounces [1 cup] of the cooked rice from the casserole and place it in a medium-sized bowl. Add the remainder of the melted butter and the dissolved saffron threads to the rice. Stir well. Set aside.
Arrange half the remaining rice in the casserole on the base of a serving platter and place the chicken pieces with the onions on top. Cover the meat with the cherries and the remaining rice and sprinkle the saffron rice on top and around the edge.

Chicken Liver Pilaff is easy to prepare and makes a good dinner party dish.

Vegetable pilaff

Served with fried chicken this makes an excellent family lunch or supper dish.
Preparation and cooking time:
45 minutes
SERVES 4-6

2 fl. oz. [$\frac{1}{4}$ cup] **vegetable oil**
4 medium-sized carrots, scraped and sliced
4 medium-sized onions, 3 thinly sliced and 1 sliced and pushed out into rings
2 medium-sized potatoes, sliced
9 oz. [$1\frac{1}{2}$ cups] **long-grain brown rice, washed, soaked in cold water for 30 minutes and drained**
1 teaspoon sea salt
1 teaspoon freshly ground black pepper
1 teaspoon dried dill leaves
1 pint [$2\frac{1}{2}$ cups] **water**
8 fl. oz. [1 cup] **vegetable stock**

Heat the oil in a large saucepan over moderate heat. When the oil is hot, add the carrots, the three sliced onions and the potatoes. Cook, stirring occasionally, for 8 minutes, or until the vegetables have softened but are not brown. Stir in the rice and, stirring constantly, cook for 2 minutes.
Stir in the salt, pepper and dill. Add the stock and the water and increase the heat to high. Bring the mixture to the boil. Reduce the heat to low, cover the pan and simmer for 20 to 25 minutes, or until the rice is tender and all the liquid has been absorbed.
Transfer the mixture to a deep serving dish. Scatter the onion rings on top and serve immediately.

fresh & dried fruits

Roughage, vitamin C, vitamin B, and natural sugars are all supplied by fruits. To give balance and nourishment every meal should include a fresh fruit, fruit juice or fruit-based dessert. Children should be encouraged to enjoy fresh fruits and offered fruit as the ideal between-meals snack. And if you cannot persuade the men in the family to eat fruit raw, then serve it in the guise of tasty, filling pies and puddings.

Add fruits to salads and meat dishes. Orange segments go well with liver as well as with the traditional duck, apples are the classic accompaniment to pork, pineapple tastes marvellous with ham. Buy fruits with care. Look for firm, fresh apples and pears, unbruised bananas, plump succulent soft fruits. If you grow your own fruit pick it at the last minute before cooking or deep-freeze it quickly for future use.

Keep a good supply of dried fruits like apricots, figs and dates. These are useful for desserts and for simple, but delicious, fruit compôtes which taste marvellous with honey and fresh cream.

Coconut apples

Baked apples are delicious with a sweet filling. This one is made with creamy coconut and iron-rich apricots.
Preparation and cooking time:
1 hour 20 minutes
S E R V E S 4

4 large cooking apples
2 oz. [⅓ cup] dried apricots
4 oz. creamed coconut, available from speciality shops
2 oz. [½ cup] stale cake crumbs
3 tablespoons honey
5 fl. oz. [⅝ cup] water

Heat the oven to 350°F (Gas Mark 4, 180°C).
Wash the apples well and core them, replacing the section of core from the base as a 'stopper' for the filling.

Pour boiling water over the apricots, leave for 10 minutes, then drain them and snip or chop into small pieces.
Meanwhile, put the creamed coconut through a coarse mill or grinder, combine half with the cake crumbs and 2 tablespoons of the honey. Stir in the chopped apricots and stuff the apples with the mixture. Make a slit with a sharp knife round the middle of each apple to prevent bursting.
Place the apples in a shallow baking dish. Pour the remaining tablespoon of honey and the water around them and cook for 1 hour or until apples are soft. Baste occasionally and add more water and honey if necessary.
Serve hot or cold, with the rest of the coconut beaten to a cream with a little water.

Date and orange salad

This light, refreshing dessert is ideal to round off a substantial meal. It may be served alone or with cream, sour cream or yogurt.
Preparation and cooking time:
1 hour, plus chilling time
S E R V E S 4

4 oz. [⅔ cup] dried figs
½ tablespoon soft brown sugar
3 large oranges
12 dessert dates
4 tablespoons maple syrup

Wash the figs well. Put them in a pan with the sugar. Add enough boiling water to cover. Soak for 30 minutes, then simmer gently for 5 minutes. Remove the figs with a perforated spoon. Boil up liquid and reduce slightly. Cool and reserve.
Peel the oranges, remove all pith and slice thinly with a sharp knife. Arrange in a shallow serving dish.
Stone the dates. Snip stems from figs. Chop the fruit roughly and scatter over oranges. Spoon the maple syrup over, together with 2 tablespoons reserved syrup from the figs.
Chill lightly before serving.

Fig and apple pie

Apple pie is a favourite standby, and it is a good idea to have a new version sometimes to offer hungry families.

Preparation and cooking time:
1 hour 10 minutes
S E R V E S 4

8 oz. dried figs
8 oz. cooking apples
2 tablespoons soft brown sugar
4 tablespoons marmalade
For the pastry:
8 oz. [2 cups] flour
pinch of sea salt
4 oz. [½ cup] margarine
water

Heat the oven to 425°F (Gas Mark 7, 220°C).
Meanwhile, wash the figs well, cover with boiling water and leave to soak for 30 minutes.
Sift the flour and salt together, rub in margarine and add just enough water to make a firm dough. Roll out and use half to line a greased pie plate.
Peel, core and slice the apples. Drain the figs and snip off their stalks. Chop roughly. Place the figs in the pie plate with the apples, sprinkle with sugar and top with the marmalade. Roll out the remaining pastry, cover pie, seal and trim the edges.
Bake for 15 minutes, then lower heat to 350°F (Gas Mark 4, 180°C) for a further 15-20 minutes, or until the pie crust is golden brown.

Strawberries with caramel topping

This is a light summer dessert to make when strawberries are at their best.
Preparation and cooking time:
15 minutes, plus 1 hour chilling time
S E R V E S 4

1 lb. ripe strawberries
2 tablespoons soft brown sugar
grated zest of 1 orange
10 fl. oz. [1¼ cups] natural yogurt
2-4 oz. demerara [¼-½ cup light brown] sugar

Hull and wash the strawberries. Drain and pat dry. Toss in the soft brown sugar and arrange in a shallow fireproof dish.
Heat the grill [broiler].
Mix the orange zest into the yogurt and spread over the strawberries. Sprinkle the demerara sugar over the yogurt in an even layer and place under the hot grill [broiler] until the sugar melts. Cool the dish.
Chill for 1 hour, so that the sugar forms a crisp caramel topping.

beans & lentils

Beans are not only cheap and filling they are also a rich source of protein, vitamins and minerals (sodium, potassium, magnesium, phosphorus, sulphur). By adding lentils, soya or kidney beans to a meat dish or soup you effectively double the nutritional value of the dish. So when budgeting is difficult it is a good idea to choose cheaper cuts of meat and add beans to give more nourishment to the finished dish. Always keep dried beans in your store-cupboard for a good standby when a hot, tasty main course or soup is required.

Remember that all dried pulses need soaking overnight before use. Use a good-sized pot and make sure the water level is double the depth of the beans.

Braised beef rolls with beans

This is a delicious way of cooking the less expensive cuts of beef. These are just as nutritious as the more expensive cuts and this dish is made even more so by the addition of beans.
Preparation and cooking time:
3½ hours
S E R V E S 4

2 oz. [¼ cup] **red kidney beans, soaked overnight**
1½ lb. **lean braising steak**
4 slices **streaky bacon**
mustard to taste
4 oz. [⅔ cup] **prunes, soaked overnight**
2 tablespoons **vegetable oil**
2 **celery stalks**
2 oz. **mushrooms**
1 medium-sized **onion**
2 teaspoons **sea salt**
¼ teaspoon **freshly ground black pepper**
water or stock

Simmer the beans in fresh, unsalted water until tender (about 1½ hours). Drain and reserve.
Heat the oven to 350°F (Gas Mark 4, 180°C).
Trim the steak, beat it out until very thin and divide into 8 slices. De-rind the bacon and cut each slice in half. Lay a piece on each beef slice and smear well with prepared mustard.
Drain the prunes, stone them and snip into small pieces with kitchen scissors. Divide among the beef slices. Form into rolls and secure with thin string or thread. Heat the oil in a pan and brown the rolls quickly.
Wash the celery and mushrooms, peel the onion. Chop vegetables roughly and place in a deep casserole. Set the beef rolls on the bed of chopped vegetables, add seasoning and pour about half an inch of water or stock into the bottom of the dish.
Cover and cook for 1-1½ hours or until the meat is tender, adding the beans to the dish for the last half hour of cooking. Snip the thread and remove carefully from the rolls before serving.

Lentil and onion pie

This is a good dish for cooks who like to use a pre-set oven. (Prepare the ingredients the night before the meal if you wish.) As it is very filling serve with a simple green vegetable or salad and follow it with fruit.
Preparation and cooking time:
1 hour, plus 12 hours soaking time for the lentils
S E R V E S 4

12 oz. **lentils**
8 oz. **potatoes**
milk
½ oz. [1 tablespoon] **butter**
1 large **onion**
1 lb. **tomatoes**
2 oz. [4 tablespoons] **lard or dripping**
1 **bay leaf**

Soak the lentils for 12 hours or overnight and cook them in a little water for 45 minutes or until soft. Strain and mash thoroughly, add the bay leaf and set aside.
Boil the potatoes in their skins, skin and mash thoroughly with a little milk and butter.
Chop the onion and tomatoes and stew until soft in half the lard.
Heat the oven to 375°F (Gas Mark 5, 190°C).
Grease an ovenproof dish. Put in the lentils, top with the tomato and onion mixture and add the mashed potatoes. Dot with the remaining fat and bake in the oven for 30 minutes.

Lentil stew

This delicious warming stew is useful as a supper dish for a hungry family and makes an excellent standby for times when meat is not available.
Preparation and cooking time:
1½ hours, plus 12 hours soaking time for lentils
S E R V E S 4

8 oz. **brown lentils**
1 medium-sized **carrot**
2 **leeks**
1 **celery stalk**
2 large **onions**
1 small **turnip**
3 oz. [⅜ cup] **lard or dripping**
1 oz. [¼ cup] **flour**
5 fl. oz. [⅝ cup] **stock**
sea salt
freshly-ground black pepper
To garnish:
parsley, chopped

Soak the lentils for 12 hours or overnight and cook them in a little water for about 45 minutes or until almost soft.
Meanwhile cut the vegetables into small pieces. Melt half the fat in a large pan and simmer the vegetables in it for 10 minutes.
Drain off any surplus water from the lentils and add them to the vegetables.
Cook for a further 5-10 minutes, stirring to prevent sticking.
Melt the rest of the fat in a large saucepan, add the flour, stir again then add the stock, stirring all the time to make a smooth sauce. Add the lentil and vegetable mixture, season to taste and serve garnished with chopped parsley.

Red bean salad

This makes an unusual addition to a cold buffet table or cold meat dish. You do, however, have to remember to soak the beans overnight in advance.
Preparation and cooking time:
2 hours
S E R V E S 2-4

4 oz. **dried red** or **brown beans, soaked overnight**
bouquet garni of 1 bay leaf, 1 celery stalk and 4-5 parsley sprigs
1 medium-sized **onion, finely sliced**

2 ripe firm tomatoes
2 oz. [½ cup] **cheese, grated**
2 tablespoons chopped parsley
sea salt
freshly ground black pepper
For the dressing:
2 fl. oz. [¼ cup] **mayonnaise**
2 fl. oz. double [¼ cup heavy]
   cream (lightly whipped)
the grated zest and juice of ¼ lemon
¼ teaspoon dry mustard
sea salt
freshly ground black pepper

Drain the beans. Put them in a large saucepan, cover with slightly salted water and bring to the boil very slowly. Add the bouquet garni. Cover the pan and simmer for 1 hour, or until the beans are tender, adding the onion 3-4 minutes before the end of the cooking time. Drain off the liquid and put the beans and onion into a bowl.
Scald, then skin the tomatoes. Cut them in half and remove the seeds and

Braised Beef Rolls with beans look colourful and are very nutritious.

core. Add them to the bean mixture, then add the cheese, parsley and seasoning to taste.
To make the dressing stir the cream into the mayonnaise. Slowly add the lemon zest and juice, stirring continuously. Add the mustard and season well. The dressing should be a thin consistency. If the mixture is thick add 1 tablespoon of warm water.
Mix the bean mixture with the dressing and serve.

Soya bean and green pepper salad

☆ ✂

This nourishing, crunchy side salad is delicious with Cauliflower Cheese or a cheese omelette.
Preparation time:
20 minutes

SERVES 4

4 green peppers, de-seeded and cut
   into thin strips
6 spring onions [scallions],
   finely chopped
4 tablespoons olive oil
2 tablespoons dry red wine
½ garlic clove, finely chopped
½ teaspoon sea salt
¼ teaspoon freshly ground black
   pepper
4 tablespoons salted soya bean
   splits

Combine in a medium-sized salad bowl the green pepper strips and spring onions [scallions]. Set aside.
Combine the oil, wine, garlic, salt and pepper in a screw-top jar. Cover the jar and shake it for 10 seconds.
Pour this dressing over the green peppers and onions [scallions]. Toss the ingredients together thoroughly. Sprinkle over the soya bean splits and serve.

Dried beans and peas

These are the 'pulses'—dried vegetables which can be used instead of fresh ones when they are scarce, *or* as part of the main course, since they are rich in protein. Boiled lentils, for example, supply 6.8 grams of protein per 100 grams—which compares well with yogurt (4.7) and eggs (11.9).

The nutritional value of the pulse vegetables has long been recognized in hot countries round the Mediterranean, and in the Near, Middle and Far East. The fact that they can be stored for long periods without losing this value is a good point where the climate causes fresh foods to deteriorate quickly.

In France, the slow-cooking 'cassoulet'—a dish based on dried haricot beans—is a culinary classic. In Egypt, where lentils are eaten almost every day in most homes, rich spices are added to give piquancy to the fairly bland taste of the pulse vegetables.

In Russia and North East Europe, the larger brown lentils and brown beans are used for substantial family supper dishes. In Czechoslovakia, a winter soup is made from dried brown lentils soaked overnight, then cooked and sieved to make a purée. This is combined with grated onion, garlic, red pepper and rounds of smoked sausage. The result is appetizing and *very* filling—what's more, it is cheap too.

In the photograph, right, the beautiful yellows, browns and greens of the pulses make a rich mosaic of colour. Use the key below for easy identification:

1. Brown lentils
2. Red kidney beans
3. Split kalay
4. Black eye peas
5. Soya beans
6. Dutch brown beans
7. Blanched lentils
8. Azuki
9. Mung
10. Yellow split peas
11. Sugar beans
12. Black beans
13. Red lentils
14. Kalay
15. Borlotti
16. Butter (dried Lima) beans
17. Chick peas
18. Yellow split peas
19. Haricots (Canellini)
20. Green lentils
21. Lupini
22. Dried green peas

molasses

Molasses has been described as a crude mixture of sugars and minerals, and because of this natural 'crudeness' many people feel it can be a useful diet addition. However, most nutritionists say that the vitamins and minerals in molasses are readily available in other foods in sufficient quantities to provide good nutrition, and there is, therefore, no need to take molasses as a dietary supplement. On the other hand, where there is a choice between sugar and molasses—as in cooking—molasses is certainly better food-value.

Refined white sugar is extraordinarily high in carbohydrates—105 grams of sugar contains 100 grams of carbohydrates. But it contains very little else. Molasses is rich in magnesium, calcium, sodium and potassium salts, copper and the vitamins of the B group. Molasses alone will not supply sufficient quantities of these nutrients without the contribution of other foods, but it can certainly help and it is infinitely preferable to 'pure' sugar.

Jaggery or 'gur'

Indian cooks generally use jaggery whenever a sweetener is required. It is similar to molasses, can be obtained from health-food and oriental or speciality stores and is made from the juice of either the sugar cane or the palm. Sweeter than molasses, its colour ranges from dark brown to cream. In India it is used both as a food and as a medicine for rheumatism and intestinal disorders.

Minerals and vitamins in molasses	
Minerals	mg. per 100 grams
Sodium	96.0
Potassium	147
Calcium	497
Magnesium	144
Iron	9.17
Phosphorous	30.6
Sulphur	68.5
Chlorine	815
Vitamins	mg. per 100 grams
B1 (thiamine)	0.89
B2 (riboflavin)	0.3
Niacin (nicotinic acid)	4.7
Pantothenic acid	4.29
Choline	6.44

Coffee shake

☆ ⊠

This drink is almost a meal in itself. It is rich in both protein and vitamins, and if you are having it as a snack lunch you could add an egg yolk.
Preparation time: *5 minutes*
S E R V E S 1

6 fl. oz. [¾ cup] milk
½ teaspoon dried skim milk powder
1 teaspoon brewer's yeast powder
1 teaspoon molasses
1 teaspoon clear honey
1 teaspoon instant decaffeinated coffee powder
To garnish:
nutmeg

Pour the milk into the blender container. Add all the remaining ingredients and blend at full speed for 2 minutes. If you do not have a blender, place in a fairly deep bowl and whisk for 3 minutes. Pour into a glass.
Grate a little nutmeg on the surface before serving.

Molasses and chocolate cooler

☆ ⊠

Molasses blends well with milk, spices and chocolate to make this delicious and highly nutritious drink. Use it as a hot-weather treat for children or as a mid-morning pick-me-up for yourself.
Preparation time: *40 minutes*
S E R V E S 1

½ tablespoon molasses
a pinch of ground ginger
¼ teaspoon ground cinnamon
2 tablespoons hot water
6 fl. oz. [¾ cup] milk, ice cold
½ teaspoon grated plain [semi-sweet] chocolate
1 scoop vanilla ice-cream (optional)

Stir the molasses and spices into the hot water until they are well-mixed. Allow to cool.
Add the milk, sprinkle with the grated chocolate and, if liked, top with a scoop of ice-cream.

Molasses meringue

⊠

This is a spectacular dessert for special occasions when you want to impress guests with something different. The rich taste of the molasses blends well with the strawberry jam.

As this dish is very filling serve it after a fairly simple main course.
Preparation and cooking time: *45 minutes*
S E R V E S 4

8 fl. oz. [1 cup] milk
½ tablespoon molasses
2 oz. fresh wholemeal [1 cup wholewheat] breadcrumbs
2 egg yolks
3 tablespoons strawberry jam (home-made if possible)
For the meringue topping:
2 egg whites
1 tablespoon castor [fine] sugar
½ tablespoon molasses

Heat the oven to 375°F (Gas Mark 5, 190°C).
Warm the milk and dissolve the molasses in it. Place the breadcrumbs in a basin, pour in the milk mixture and allow to cool slightly. Beat the egg yolks into the breadcrumb mixture.
Transfer to a greased pie dish and allow to stand for 20 minutes. Then bake in the oven for 15-20 minutes or until firm.
Remove from the oven and allow to cool slightly. Spread with strawberry jam.
Raise the oven heat to 450°F (Gas Mark 8, 230°C).
Beat the egg whites until stiff but not dry, add castor sugar and beat again until smooth. Beat in the molasses. Spread this meringue mixture over the jam and place in the oven for 5 minutes, until top is firm and crisp.
Serve at once.

Tasting as good as a milk shake, Molasses and Chocolate Cooler is a favourite with children.

kelp-
for minerals

Kelp is a type of seaweed found on rocky ocean beds and shores. There are about 900 different species, but kelp tablets are made from the common *fucus vesiculosus*, a brownish seaweed with flat, fan-like fronds and air bubbles which children love to 'pop'.

Kelp and minerals

The real nutritional value of kelp lies in the mineral salts it contains. Trace quantities of these minerals are vital to good health, but refining and processing of other foods in which they are present often destroys them and although some are replaced at the end of the manufacturing process others are not. The importance of minerals in body metabolism is only just being fully explored, and until you know the exact amounts you need it makes sense to get your fair share or more. So, what do you get from kelp? Here is a full list: aluminium, barium, calcium, chromium, copper, iodine, lead, magnesium, manganese, potassium, silicon, silver, sodium, strontium, tin, titanium, vanadium, zinc.

Iodine is essential for the correct functioning of the thyroid gland. Copper helps the body to utilize vitamin C. Magnesium helps to keep bones and teeth strong, hair shiny and nails in good health. Manganese is vital for the nervous system and sexual drive. And so the list goes on.

The sensible, diet-conscious person would find many of these things in other foods. Green vegetables, for example, contain magnesium; liver and kidney contain manganese and copper, and seafoods are all rich sources of iodine. But these good foods are not eaten in enough quantities to ensure adequate mineral supplies. Kelp tablets can, therefore, be of great use, particularly to people who eat a lot of expensive foods—cakes, biscuits, sweets, alcohol—which contribute very little in the way of nutritional value.

Kelp as a food

Seaweed was once a common and popular addition to the diet of people living near the sea, and was eaten raw or cooked. But the idea of cooking and eating seaweed is not now to everyone's taste. The Japanese lead in the consumption of kelp, and they export to Tai Wan, Hong Kong and Singapore. The kelp is 'farmed' along the Japanese coastline. It takes about two years to mature after being sown on rocks in the sea. It is then harvested, dried and stored to be re-constructed in salted water when needed.

To Western palates kelp often seems leathery and waxy in taste, although somehow not so bad when chopped finely and added to Chinese or Japanese dishes. Consequently the most usual way of including kelp in a Western diet is to take it in tablet form or to add the dried powder to soups or stews. And it is worth remembering that a heaped teaspoon of kelp powder will make a pint of jelly which sets very quickly and is virtually tasteless, so you can use it instead of gelatine. Add fruit or vegetable juice flavouring to it.

The recommended daily dosage of kelp is one 5-grain tablet a day, or two if your nails are splitting and you have an overall feeling of lowered vitality.

Carrot and celery cocktail

☆ ⧖

This cocktail is rich in essential vitamins and minerals.
Preparation time: *5 minutes*
SERVES 1

2 celery stalks
4-5 sprigs parsley
1 large carrot
4 fl. oz. [½ cup] pure apple juice (bottled)
a pinch of kelp powder

Wash the celery and parsley and scrape the carrot. Cut them into small pieces, place in a blender container with just enough water to make the machine run smoothly.

Blend for 2 minutes at medium speed. *Strain* through a sieve, pressing out all the juice. Mix this vegetable juice with the apple juice and season to taste with kelp.

Hot cheese herbed scones [biscuits]

⧖

These make a very good accompaniment to a soup and salad lunch.
Preparation and cooking time:
30 minutes
SERVES 4

8 oz. wholewheat [2 cups wholemeal] flour
2 teaspoons baking powder
¼ teaspoon sea salt

a pinch of kelp powder
2 tablespoons margarine
4 tablespoons grated cheese
½ teaspoon dried marjoram
2 tablespoons buttermilk *or* sour milk

Heat the oven to 425°F (Gas Mark 7, 220°C).
Sift together the flour, baking powder, salt and kelp, and return to the bowl any bran left in the sieve.
Rub in the margarine, stir in the cheese and marjoram and mix to a dough with the buttermilk or sour milk. (A little more liquid may be added if necessary.)
Form into a round ¾-inch thick and cut into 4 pieces. Place on a greased baking sheet and bake for 10-12 minutes. Serve with hot butter.

Onion lentil soup

Home-made soups are comforting on a cold day. This one has the extra protein of lentils and the minerals from powdered kelp.
Preparation and cooking time:
45 minutes
S E R V E S 4

12 oz. onions
8 oz. potatoes
2 tablespoons butter

2 tablespoons lentils
2 pints [5 cups] chicken stock
1 teaspoon kelp, or to taste
To serve:
parsley, chopped
grated cheese
fried croûtons or toast triangles

Peel and roughly chop the onions and potatoes. Melt the butter in a heavy pan and cook the vegetables, covered, over low heat until softened.
Meanwhile, grind the lentils to a fine powder in grinder or blender.

Carrot and Celery Cocktail makes a refreshingly different drink.

Add the lentils and stock to the softened vegetables, bring to the boil and simmer for 15 minutes. Cool slightly, pour into a blender or food mill and reduce to a smooth purée.
Return to the pan, add a little more stock or milk if necessary, together with the seasoning of kelp powder. Bring back to boiling point, garnish with parsley and serve with cheese and croûtons or toast triangles.

apple cider vinegar

The minerals contained in apple cider vinegar are potassium, phosphorus, chlorine, sodium, magnesium, iron, fluorine and silicon—plus 'trace' amounts of several others. In the folk medicine lore of the hills of Vermont in America the potassium in apple cider vinegar is supposed to have bacteria-killing powers.

According to Doctor D. C. Jarvis, author of a best-selling book on the subject, bacteria take moisture from the body cells. But body cells contain potassium and this tends to draw moisture from bacteria. The constant fight between the body cells and the bacteria can, therefore, be tipped in favour of the body cells by taking potassium-rich foods—fruit, edible leaves, roots,

berries and apple cider vinegar. And the vinegar, Doctor Jarvis claims, is not only a good source of potassium but will also kill any bacteria lurking in the digestive tract.

Quite apart from its possible anti-bacteria powers and medicinal claims the minerals it contains make apple cider vinegar a good diet supplement. The usual recommended dose is two teaspoons mixed into a glass of water and taken once a day.

Remedies
Here is a list of some of the medicinal uses of apple cider vinegar. These cannot be vouched for, but none of them will do you any harm.

As a pick-me-up mix 2 teaspoons of apple cider vinegar and 2 teaspoons of honey in a glass of warm water and take it whenever you feel low.

For fatigue take the following: mix three teaspoons of apple cider vinegar to one cup of honey. Take two teaspoons before meals and before going to bed.

For headaches put equal parts of apple cider vinegar and water into a saucepan. Bring to the boil and inhale the vapour.

Stomach upsets and mild food poisoning may be helped by taking 1 teaspoon of apple cider vinegar every few minutes until the symptoms are eased. As a preventive measure, drink 2 teaspoons of apple cider vinegar in a glass of water before eating.

French dressing

This is the classic recipe except that apple cider vinegar is substituted for the usual wine vinegar. You can make it up in advance—in larger quantities if you like—as it keeps well in the refrigerator.
Preparation time: *5 minutes*
MAKES 1½ fluid ounces

¼ teaspoon sea salt
a pinch of freshly ground black pepper
¼ teaspoon dry mustard
1 tablespoon apple cider vinegar
2 tablespoons olive oil

Place all the ingredients in a screw-top jar and shake well. Use at once or store and re-shake before serving.

Mayonnaise

This is a fool-proof method of making a delicious mayonnaise which is in no danger of curdling.
Preparation and cooking time: *15 minutes, plus cooling time*
MAKES 1 pint [2½ cups]

1 tablespoon cornflour [cornstarch]
1 teaspoon mustard
5 fl. oz. [⅝ cup] **skimmed milk**
16 fl. oz. [2 cups] **apple cider vinegar**
2 egg yolks

Mix the cornflour [cornstarch] and mustard to a smooth cream with a little of the milk. Add the remainder of the milk and the vinegar. Stir in the egg yolks. Pour the mixture into a thick-bottomed saucepan, or a double saucepan if you have one, and heat gently stirring all the time until it thickens. Do not let it boil.
Allow to cool before serving.

Mousseline dressing

This is an attractive pink dressing to serve with fish dishes or a party salad platter. The tabasco gives a piquant flavour.
Preparation time: *5 minutes*
MAKES 11 fluid ounces

5 fl. oz. double [⅝ cup heavy] **cream**
5 fl. oz. [⅝ cup] **home-made mayonnaise*** (recipe above)
1 teaspoon chopped fresh chives
1 teaspoon grated lemon zest
freshly ground black pepper
1 tablespoon tomato purée
1 tablespoon lemon juice
tabasco sauce

Fold the cream into the mayonnaise, combining well.
Add the chives, lemon zest and a little pepper. Then add tomato purée, lemon juice and a dash of tabasco to taste.

honey-energy food

Because it is easy to digest, honey is a good food for the very young and the elderly. There are many stories of exceptional longevity apparently caused by taking honey every day. And many athletes find it a good source of 'instant' energy.

How honey is made

Honey is nature's own manufactured food; harvested, processed and packed by bees. Bees are industrious little creatures. They have to be, because it takes about ten thousand flights—average length about two miles—for bees to bring a pound of nectar back to the hive. And nectar loses half its weight in evaporation!

The bee settles on a flower and sucks in the nectar. This passes into its honey sac and is mixed with acid secretions. Back at the hive the bee drops the nectar into honey 'houses'. (The biggest hive ever found was perched at the top of a giant eucalyptus tree in the Australian bush, it was 36 feet high, 21 feet across and weighed a ton.) From the 'houses' the nectar goes into honey vats and finally into the hexagonal cells of the wax honeycomb. The cells themselves are a remarkable achievement: accurate to within a thousandth of an inch, always identical and able to withstand temperatures of up to 140°F (60°C).

The flavour and texture of individual types of honey depends on the source of the nectar. Clover, heather, apple blossom and orange blossom are all popular kinds.

What honey contains

Honey contains three varieties of sugar: fructose, glucose and sucrose. The first, fructose, is a white crystalline substance which melts at 187°F (86°C). (It is sometimes called grape sugar as it is also found in grapes.) Glucose is the simplest of sugars. It is found in the blood of live animals (including humans), fruit and plant juices. Sucrose is the same as cane or beet sugar, and is a combination of fructose and glucose.

So, if honey is mainly a composition of three sugars, why is it reputed to have 'magical' properties? The known 'extras' in honey are the minerals—calcium, iron, phosphates, magnesium and iodine—and traces of at least six vitamins—B1, B2, C, pantothenic acid, pyridoxine and niacin. Then there are the 'undetermined residues' — resins, gums, etc.

Because it contains these important extras, honey is certainly a good choice as a sweetening ingredient in cooking. It is versatile, too. Honey vinegar and mead are two important by-products. Honey vinegar makes quite a good salad dressing. (You can make it yourself by boiling five parts of water to one of honey in an earthenware dish, adding a little yeast and leaving it to ferment for a few weeks in a warm room.)

Honey biscuits [cookies]

These biscuits [cookies] taste marvellous with mid-morning coffee or tea.
Preparation and cooking time:
45 minutes
MAKES 20 biscuits [cookies]

2½ oz. [5 tablespoons] **butter**
2 tablespoons **sugar**
2 tablespoons **honey**
6 oz. [1½ cups] **flour, sifted**
1½ teaspoons **baking powder**
1 teaspoon **cinnamon**
a pinch of **salt**

Heat the oven to 350°F (Gas Mark 4, 180°C).
Cream together butter and sugar. Add honey and work into the mixture with the flour, baking powder, cinnamon and salt. Roll out on a floured board to a ¾-inch thickness.
Cut into 40 small rounds, place on a greased baking sheet and bake for 10 minutes.
Allow to cool then sandwich rounds together in pairs, putting a little honey between each pair.
Serve immediately.

Honey raisin pudding

This delicious steamed pudding includes energy-giving honey and dried fruits plus extra bran, so it is very good for you.
Preparation and cooking time:
1¼ hours
SERVES 4-6

4 oz. [½ cup] **margarine**
4 oz. [¾ cup] **soft brown sugar**
2 **eggs**
3 oz. [¾ cup] **flour**
½ teaspoon **baking powder**
1 oz. [¼ cup] **bran**
4 tablespoons **raisins**
4 tablespoons **clear honey**

Cream together margarine and sugar. Beat in the eggs one at a time, adding a little flour between additions. Fold in the remaining flour, the baking powder and bran. Stir in the raisins.
Grease a large pudding basin, spoon in the honey and top with the pudding mixture so that the basin is not more than two-thirds full. Cover with foil and steam for 1 hour.
Turn out and serve with extra honey and yogurt, or cream if preferred.

Mead

Although you have to wait a long time before drinking your mead the results are well worth while.
MAKES 1 gallon

3 lb. **honey**
the grated zest of 1 **lemon**
1 gallon cold **water**
2 **egg whites**
¼ oz. **fresh yeast**

Put the honey and grated lemon zest into a large saucepan or preserving pan and add the water. Beat the whites of the eggs until frothy and add to the pan. Place it over a low heat and stir as the mixture comes to the boil. Simmer gently for 1 hour.
Pour the liquid into a large bowl and leave until lukewarm. Stir in the yeast. Cover and leave in a warm place for three days, stirring daily.
Strain the liquid through muslin and bottle. Put the corks in loosely and take care they do not work out as the mead ferments. Gradually push them in tighter as fermentation slows down.
Store the bottles in a cold place for at least a year before drinking.

Muesli

☆ ◫ ◫ ◫

This is one version of the popular
Swiss breakfast food.
Preparation time:
*10 minutes, plus 12 hours soaking
time for oats*
S E R V E S 1

1 tablespoon oat flakes or oatmeal
3 tablespoons water
1 tablespoon lemon juice
1 cup milk, mixed with 1
  tablespoon honey
1 large apple
1 tablespoon grated nuts

Soak the oats or oatmeal in the water
for about 12 hours, or overnight.
Mix together the lemon juice and the
milk and honey mixture and pour this
over the oats. Wash the apple, remove
stalk and core and grate into the
mixture. Top with grated nuts and
serve at once.

Sesame honey scones
[biscuits]

◫

The tiny sesame seed is rich in
proteins, vitamins and minerals.
Preparation and cooking time:
30 minutes
S E R V E S 4

8 oz. [2 cups] flour
2 teaspoons baking powder
½ teaspoon sea salt
2 tablespoons margarine
4 tablespoons wheat germ
2 tablespoons soft brown sugar
1 tablespoon sesame seeds
2 tablespoons clear honey
3 fl. oz. [⅜ cup] buttermilk *or*
  sour milk

Heat the oven to 425°F (Gas Mark 7,
220°C).
Sift the flour with the baking powder
and salt. Rub in the margarine, then
stir in the wheat germ, sugar and half
the sesame seeds.
Stir in the honey and buttermilk or
sour milk and mix to a dough.
Form into a round ¾-inch thick and cut
into 4 pieces. Scatter the rest of the
sesame seeds over the top. Bake on a
greased sheet for 10-15 minutes. Cool
on a wire tray. Serve split in half and
spread with butter

*Honey Biscuits [cookies] and Sesame
Honey Scones [biscuits] are ideal for an
energy-giving mid-morning break.*

yeast & wheat germ-bread

Bread is no longer, nutritionally-speaking, considered to be 'the staff of life'. In affluent Western society we eat a variety of foods which contribute to a balanced diet, so most of us do not rely on bread as the main source of nutrients. It would, however, be wrong to play down the importance of bread as a top contributor to efficient body metabolism, particularly as most people eat some bread every day—something which cannot be said of any other food.

However, not all breads are equally good for you. Wholemeal [wholewheat] bread is best (see flour chart) because not only does it contain the vitamin B found in yeast but it also gives you the added goodness of wheat germ. And it tastes better, too, as you will discover when you try some of the recipes below.

Yeast—rich source of vitamin B

'Yeast' is the group name given to microscopic organisms or fungi which are carried from the soil to plants by the wind or by insects. Yeast is a living thing. When it is 'fed' on a sugar solution the cells which make up the organism divide and re-divide very rapidly producing alcohol and carbon dioxide. This process is called fermentation.

In the preparation of alcoholic drinks the sugar solution usually consists of fruit, grain or molasses together with water; the yeast is added and the alcohol which results is retained, while the carbon dioxide is given off. In bread-making, however, the reverse occurs. The yeast action traps the 'bubbles' of carbon dioxide in the bread—making it rise—and the alcohol is released.

The history of yeast

Yeast has been used as a fermentation agent for many centuries—there is even a reference to it as a cure for constipation in a scroll dating from the Egyptian 18th Dynasty (1567—1320 BC). Until comparatively recently, however, yeast was simply accepted, it was not understood.

Wild yeast was used for making wines and breads up until the 1870s then Emil Christian Hansen, a Danish scientist, discovered that it was possible to cultivate a pure strain of yeast. After that it was found that the live yeast fungi could be dried and later reconstituted with water without losing its 'living' properties. (Until then, housewives had been using liquid yeast bought from the local bakery, and this was messy and difficult to store.) In the 1930s when vitamin B was discovered, yeast turned out to be one of its best sources.

Vitamin value

The types of yeast commonly used today are *Torula utilis*, food yeast, and *Saccharomyces cerevisiae*, brewer's and baker's yeast. As a food supplement brewer's yeast is richest in protein containing all 15 members of the valuable B complex. It is a superb source of riboflavin and nicotinic acid and is second only to peanuts as a source of thiamine. Riboflavin is particularly important for normal growth of skin, nails and hair, and trichologists often recommend yeast tablets for hair in poor condition.

The importance of yeast depends upon what else you eat. Other rich sources of vitamin B exist, but where these are excluded from the diet because of personal taste or, as in some countries, poverty, then yeast can be a superb food supplement. Take it dried and sprinkled on milk, soups, salads and casserole dishes or in tablet form. And use it in home-made bread.

Wheat germ—the most valuable part of grain

Wheat germ is a rich source of vitamins A and E and of those of the B complex, and so it can be a very valuable part of your diet. (See pages 6-7 for the importance of these vitamins.) The wheat germ contains more than 50 per cent of all the vitamins found in the grain and is the only part that contains vitamin A.

To get a clear picture of exactly what wheat germ is, imagine a grain of wheat cut in half. There are three main parts: the bran, which makes up about 13-15 per cent of the grain, is a protective outer covering, difficult to digest for some people but a valuable source of roughage; the endosperm, which makes up about 82-86 per cent of the grain, consists mainly of starch and helps the grain to germinate and the seedling to develop; and, finally, the germ. This is a small part of the whole—only about 2.2-2.9 per cent. It is straw-coloured, a rich source of vitamin A, B and E and alive.

Unfortunately the general preference for white, light, easily-digestible bread means taking away this vitamin-rich wheat germ and bran—this is what gives wholemeal [wholewheat] bread its rough, nutty taste.

Vitamin value

As a dietary supplement, wheat germ can play an important part in maintaining good health—especially for the many people whose basic diet is fairly low in vitamins B and E. (The vitamin A contained in wheat germ is certainly of value but the quantity is less than half that present in a comparable amount of the fish liver oils.) It makes sense to get your fair share of these two valuable vitamins. A good way of doing so is either to eat wholemeal [wholewheat] bread or use wheat germ in cooking or sprinkled on food. Wheat germ gives a pleasantly nutty flavour and crunchy texture to foods, especially when used on cereals or stirred into fruit and vegetable juices. You could try it, too, cooked just as if it were a form of porridge and served with honey and milk as a breakfast food. If, however, you honestly dislike the taste, then you can take wheat germ oil in capsule form.

Caraway knots

Baps

⧖ ⧖ ⧖

These soft, white, breakfast rolls are best served hot from the oven with lots of butter.
Preparation and cooking time:
3½ hours
MAKES 8 baps

½ oz. fresh yeast
½ teaspoon sugar
5 fl. oz. [⅝ cup] lukewarm water
5 fl. oz. [⅝ cup] plus 2 tablespoons milk
2 oz. [¼ cup] plus 1 teaspoon butter *or* margarine
1 lb. [4 cups] plus 1 tablespoon flour
½ teaspoon sea salt

Crumble the yeast into a small mixing bowl and mash in the sugar with a kitchen fork. Add 2 tablespoons of the lukewarm water and cream the yeast and water together. Set the bowl aside in a warm, draught-free place for 15 to 20 minutes or until the yeast mixture has risen and is puffed up and frothy.
Meanwhile, in a small saucepan, scald 5 fluid ounces [⅝ cup] of the milk over moderate heat. Do this by bringing it to just under boiling point. Remove the pan from the heat and add 2 ounces [¼ cup] of the butter or margarine. Set the pan aside to allow the milk to cool to lukewarm.
Sift the 1 pound [4 cups] of flour and the salt into a large, warmed mixing bowl. Make a well in the centre of the flour and add the yeast and milk mixture and the remaining water. Using your fingers or a spatula, gradually draw the flour into the liquid. Continue mixing until all the flour is incorporated and the dough comes away from the sides of the bowl.
Turn the dough out onto a lightly floured surface and knead it for 10 minutes, reflouring the surface if the dough becomes sticky. It should be smooth and elastic.
Rinse, thoroughly dry and lightly grease the large mixing bowl. Form the dough into a ball and return it to the bowl. Cover the bowl with a clean cloth and set it aside in a warm, draught-free place for 1 to 1½ hours or until the dough has risen and doubled in bulk.
Lightly grease a large baking sheet with the teaspoon of butter or margarine and coat it with the

Making your own bread is simpler than it sounds—and it is well worthwhile.

tablespoon of flour. Set aside.
Turn the risen dough out onto a lightly floured surface and knead it for 5 minutes. Divide the dough into eight equal pieces and pat and roll each piece into an oval shape. Flatten each oval and place it on the prepared baking sheet. Cover with a clean cloth and set aside in a warm, draught-free place for 30 minutes.
Heat the oven to 425°F (Gas Mark 7, 220°C).
Brush each bap with the remaining 2 tablespoons of milk and place the baking sheet in the oven. Bake the baps for 15-20 minutes or until they are golden brown.

Caraway knots

⧖ ⧖ ⧖

These popular savoury knots are delicious served warm with butter.
Preparation and cooking time:
3 hours
MAKES 20 knots

¾ oz. fresh yeast
1 tablespoon sugar
2 teaspoons lukewarm water
15 fl. oz. [1⅞ cups] milk
2 oz. [¼ cup] butter or margarine
2 lb. [8 cups] plus 1 tablespoon flour
1 tablespoon sea salt
2 eggs
3 tablespoons caraway seeds
1 teaspoon vegetable oil

Crumble the yeast into a small mixing bowl and mash in 1 teaspoon of the sugar with a kitchen fork. Add the warm water and cream the yeast and water together. Set the bowl aside in a warm, draught-free place for 15 to 20 minutes or until the yeast mixture has risen and is puffed up and frothy.
Pour the milk into a small saucepan, place it over low heat, and bring it to just under boiling point. Remove the pan from the heat and add the butter or margarine. When the butter or margarine has melted, set the pan aside and leave the milk to cool to lukewarm.
Sift the 2 pounds [8 cups] of flour, the salt and the remaining sugar into a medium-sized mixing bowl. Make a well in the centre and pour in the yeast mixture and milk mixture. Add one of the eggs. Using a wooden spoon or your hands, gradually incorporate the flour into the liquid. Continue mixing until a smooth dough is formed.
Fold in 2 tablespoons of caraway

seeds. Sprinkle the remaining flour over the dough. Cover the bowl with a cloth and put it in a warm, draught-free place to rise for 1 to 1½ hours or until the dough has almost doubled in bulk.
Turn the risen dough out on to a lightly floured surface and knead it for about 5 minutes or until it is smooth.
Roll the dough into a 12-inch long roll and with a sharp knife slice it into 20 equal pieces. Roll one piece between your hands to make a thin rope about 14 inches long. Place the rope on a board and shape it into a loop with its ends crossed. Turn the ends of the rope over again to make a twist at the base of the loop. Spread the tips of the two ends apart, bring the loop over to them and pinch the tips to the loop. Do the same with each piece of dough. After all the knots have been formed, leave them to rest for 10 minutes.
Using a pastry brush, lightly grease two baking sheets with the oil. Set aside.
Fill a large saucepan two-thirds full of water. Bring the water to the boil over high heat. Lay 2 knots at a time in the water. The knots will sink to the bottom, and then rise to the surface of the water and will double in size.
With a slotted spoon, carefully transfer the knots from the water to the greased baking sheets. (If the knots have come untwisted, gently press them into their original shape.)
Leave the knots in a warm place for 15 minutes or until they are almost dry.
Heat the oven to 400°F (Gas Mark 6, 200°C).
Beat the remaining egg. Using a pastry brush, coat the knots with the beaten egg and sprinkle them with the rest of the caraway seeds. Place the knots in the oven and bake them for 15 to 20 minutes, or until they are golden brown.
Remove the knots from the oven and transfer them to a wire rack. Serve warm.

One rise brown loaf

⧖ ⧖

This loaf needs less rising time than most bread recipes, but it will not keep for as long as other breads. Eat it the day you bake it if possible.
Preparation and cooking time:
1¾ hours

MAKES 1 x 2lb. loaf

½ teaspoon sugar
15 fl. oz. [1⅞ cups] tepid water
  (110°F, 43°C)
1 tablespoon dried yeast
12 oz. wholemeal
  [3 cups wholewheat] flour
12 oz. [3 cups] flour
2 teaspoons sea salt
2 teaspoons oil

Prepare the yeast liquid. Dissolve the sugar in the warm water, sprinkle in the yeast and leave for ten minutes or until frothy.
Sift together the flours and salt, and return to the bowl any bran left in the sieve. Add the oil and work in the yeast liquid to make a firm ball of dough which comes away from the sides of the bowl. Knead well on a lightly floured surface for 5 minutes.
Heat the oven to 475°F (Gas Mark 8, 240°C).
Place the dough in a greased 2-pound loaf tin, slip into a large oiled plastic bag and leave to rise in a warm place for about 1 hour or until doubled in bulk. When sufficiently risen, the dough should spring back when lightly pressed.
Bake in oven for ten minutes then reduce oven temperature to 425°F (Gas Mark 7, 220°C) and bake for a further 35 minutes, or until brown. Cool on a wire tray.

Sour dough bread

☒ ☒ ☒

This delicious bread is based upon the Bavarian recipe, not the American one. It will keep for a week or more if stored in a bread bin or crock.
Preparation and cooking time:
4½ hours, plus 4 to 5 days for the sour dough starter
MAKES 2 x 2lb. loaves
  or 4 x 1lb. loaves

1 oz. fresh *or* dried yeast
¼ teaspoon sugar
1½ pints [3 cups] water, lukewarm
1½ lb. [6 cups] strong plain
  [all-purpose] flour *or* stoneground
  wholemeal [wholewheat] flour
1½ lb. [6 cups] stoneground rye
  flour
4 oz. [½ cup] cracked wheat
1½ tablespoons dark brown sugar
1½ tablespoons coarse rock salt.
2 tablespoons vegetable oil
1½ tablespoons culinary malt
  (optional)

For the sour dough starter:
8 oz. strong plain
  [2 cups all-purpose] flour
8 oz. [2 cups] stoneground rye flour
4 oz. [½ cup] sugar
16 fl. oz. [2 cups] milk
For the glaze:
1 egg, beaten
2 teaspoons cold water

Put all the ingredients for the sour dough starter into a large screw top jar or container with a tight lid. Mix it well with a fork. Screw on the lid and leave it undisturbed at room temperature for 4-5 days.
Grease loaf tins with butter and set aside.
Crumble the yeast in a small bowl and mash in ¼ teaspoon sugar with a kitchen fork. Add 10 fluid ounces [1¼ cups] of the water and mix together. Set aside in a warm, draught-free place for 15-20 minutes or until the yeast has risen and is puffed up and frothy.
Put the flours, cracked wheat, dark brown sugar and salt into a very large mixing bowl. Mix well together.
Add the vegetable oil, and culinary malt if you are using it, to the remaining water and mix together.
Make a well in the centre of the flour mixture, pour in the yeast mixture, the water, malt and oil mixture and the sour dough starter. Using your fingers or a spatula mix well together until all the flour is incorporated and the dough comes away from the sides of the bowl.
Turn the dough on to a floured surface and knead for about 5 minutes.
Rinse, thoroughly dry and lightly grease the large mixing bowl. Shape the dough into a ball and return it to the bowl. Dust the top of the dough with flour and cover the bowl with a clean damp cloth. Set aside in a warm, draught-free place and leave to rise for 1½-2 hours or until the dough has risen and almost doubled in bulk.
Turn the dough out on to a floured surface and knead again for 8-10 minutes. Using a sharp knife cut it into required loaf sizes, put it into the greased tins, cover with a damp cloth and leave in a warm place to rise again for another 1 to 1½ hours.
Heat the oven to 475°F (Gas Mark 9, 240°C).
Mix together the egg and water glazing and paint the top of the loaves with it.
Place tins in centre of oven and bake for 10 minutes. Then lower oven temperature to 425°F (Gas Mark 7,

220°C) put the bread on a lower shelf and bake for another 30-40 minutes. Remove the loaves from the oven, tip them out and tap the undersides with your knuckles. If the bread sounds hollow like a drum it is cooked. If not, return to the oven for a further 10 minutes.
Cool the loaves on a wire rack.

Wholemeal [wholewheat] bread

☒ ☒ ☒

This bread is simple to make at home. It is fragrant and delicious and retains all the goodness of the wheat.
Preparation and cooking time:
3 hours
MAKES 2 x 1 lb. loaves

½ teaspoon sugar
15 fl. oz. [1⅞ cups] tepid water
  (110°F, 43°C)
1 tablespoon dried yeast
1½ lb. wholemeal [6 cups
  wholewheat] flour
½ tablespoon sea salt
2 teaspoons oil
1 tablespoon soft brown sugar

Prepare the yeast liquid. Dissolve the sugar in the warm water, sprinkle in the yeast and leave for 10 minutes or until frothy.
Sift together the flour and salt, and return to the bowl any residue left in the sieve. Mix in oil and sugar. Work in the yeast liquid to make a firm ball of dough which comes away from the sides of the bowl. Knead thoroughly on a lightly floured surface for about 10 minutes until the dough is smooth and elastic.
Replace in bowl, cover with a large greased plastic bag and leave in a warm place for 1 hour or until risen to double its bulk. The dough should spring back when gently pressed.
Heat the oven to 475°F (Gas Mark 9, 240°C).
Turn out and knead well, flattening with the knuckles to knock out air bubbles. Place in 2 greased 1-pound loaf tins, replace in loose plastic bag leaving plenty of air space. Leave to rise again for one hour or until doubled in bulk.
Bake in the oven for 10 minutes then lower the oven temperature to 425°F (Gas Mark 7, 220°C), and bake for a further 35 minutes. When done, the loaf will shrink from the sides of the tin, and will sound hollow if tapped. Cool on wire tray.

flour-cakes

There is, as every cook knows, a tremendous difference between cakes you buy and those you make. Home-made cakes taste better for a start and you can make sure that they are nutritious as well, particularly if you choose your flour carefully.

Flour

Flours vary in composition. Broadly-speaking, they are defined by their rate of 'extraction'. This means the percentage of the whole grain (or wheat germ) which remains in the flour after milling. For example, wholemeal flours (wholewheat is another name for them) contain the *whole* of the cleaned wheat germ; brown or wheatmeal flours usually contain about 80 per cent to 90 per cent; white flours usually contain 70 to 72 per cent, and 'patent' flours (very white in colour) contain only 40-50 per cent of the germ. (If you can it is a good idea to use 80 per cent extraction flour when trying the recipes given here.)

Over, there is a table giving the comparative values of four different kinds of flour. (The dramatic increase in calcium in the whiter flours is due to calcium—in the form of chalk—being added during the refining processes.)

Banana nut bread

⊠ ⊠

Tea breads are very simple to make and are always popular with a family.
Preparation and cooking time:
1 hour 15 minutes
MAKES 1 x 1 lb. loaf

2 oz. [¼ cup] **margarine**
2 oz. [⅓ cup] **soft brown sugar**
8 oz. [2 cups] **flour**
1 teaspoon **baking powder**
½ teaspoon **sea salt**
1 **egg**
2 ripe **bananas**
2 tablespoons **natural yogurt**
1 tablespoon **clear honey**
2 oz. [½ cup] **chopped walnuts**

Heat the oven to 350°F (Gas Mark 4, 180°C).
Cream the margarine with sugar.
Sift together the flour, baking powder and salt. Beat the egg into the fat with a little flour.
Mash the bananas, beat in with the yogurt and honey and gradually add to the egg mixture with the rest of the flour. Stir in the nuts.
Turn into a greased loaf tin and bake for 1¼-1½ hours, or until a skewer comes out clean when inserted. Cool on a wire tray and keep for 24 hours before cutting.

Ginger fruit cake

⊠ ⊠

Sweetened with iron-rich black treacle [molasses], this cake is good for family snacks. Try it, too, with cheese for a picnic lunch.
Preparation and cooking time:
1¼ hours
MAKES 1 x 9-inch cake

4 oz. [½ cup] **margarine**
4 oz. [⅔ cup] **soft brown sugar**
8 oz. [2 cups] **flour**
1 teaspoon **baking powder**
1 teaspoon **ground ginger**
¼ teaspoon **ground cinnamon**
¼ teaspoon **sea salt**
2 **eggs**
5 fl. oz. **black treacle**
  [⅝ cup **molasses**]
3 fl. oz. [⅜ cup] **clear honey**
2 tablespoons **buttermilk** *or* **sour milk**
2 oz. [⅓ cup] **raisins**
2 oz. [⅓ cup] **cooking dates, chopped**
6-8 **almonds, blanched and shredded**

Heat the oven to 325°F, (Gas Mark 3, 170°C).
Cream together the margarine and sugar until fluffy.
Sift together the flour, baking powder, spices and salt. Beat the eggs into the fat, one at a time, adding half the flour. Beat the treacle, honey and buttermilk into the mixture and add the rest of the flour. Stir in the fruit.
Turn mixture into a greased 9-inch square cake tin and bake for 50-60 minutes, or until a skewer comes out clean. Sprinkle the almonds over the top after 40 minutes' cooking time.
Cool the cake on a wire tray and keep for 24 hours before cutting into squares.

Peanut coffee sandwich cake

⊠ ⊠

This cake includes the extra nourishment of peanuts and soya flour, plus a delicious and unusual filling.
Preparation and cooking time:
50 minutes, plus cooling time
MAKES 1 x 8-inch cake

7 oz. [⅞ cup] **margarine**
7 oz. [1¼ cups] **soft brown sugar**
6 oz. [1½ cups] **flour**
1 teaspoon **baking powder**
4 tablespoons **soya flour**
3 large **eggs**
For the filling:
2 tablespoons **smooth peanut butter**
2 tablespoons **honey**
1 teaspoon **decaffeinated instant coffee powder**

Heat the oven to 350°F (Gas Mark 4, 180°C).
Cream the margarine and sugar thoroughly together.
Sift the flour with baking powder and soya. Beat eggs into the fat one at a time, adding a little flour between each one. Beat well, then fold in the remaining flour. Divide between two greased 8-inch sandwich tins.
Bake for 30 to 35 minutes, until the cake is well risen and when you insert a skewer it comes out clean. Cool on a wire rack.
To make the filling, beat the peanut butter and honey together. Dissolve the coffee in a teaspoon of boiling water and work into the honey mixture.

Sandringham tarts

Make these in small patty tins for mid-afternoon break. Alternatively, you can use the same mixture as the filling for an open tart for dessert.
Preparation and cooking time:
40 minutes
MAKES 12 tarts

For the pastry:
4 oz. [1 cup] flour
a pinch of sea salt
2 oz. [¼ cup] margarine
water
For the filling:
3 oz. [⅜ cup] margarine
3 oz. [½ cup] soft brown sugar
1 egg
3 oz. [¾ cup] ground unpolished rice
raspberry jam

Heat the oven to 400°F (Gas Mark 6, 200°C).
Sift together the flour and salt, rub in the margarine and add enough cold water to make a stiff dough. Roll out and use to line 12 patty tins.
To make the filling, cream together the margarine and sugar. Beat in the egg and the ground rice (unpolished rice may be ground at home in small quantities in a blender or grinder).
Place a teaspoonful of jam in the bottom of each tart. Divide the rice mixture between them and smooth over to cover the jam. Bake for 12-15 minutes. Cool on a wire rack.

Seed cake

This traditional caraway cake is always a favourite.
Preparation and cooking time:
2 hours
MAKES 1 x 1lb. cake

4 oz. [½ cup] butter
4 oz. castor [½ cup fine] sugar
2 eggs, beaten
8 oz. [2 cups] flour
2 teaspoons baking powder
2 teaspoons caraway seeds
4 tablespoons milk

Heat the oven to 350°F (Gas Mark 4, 180°C).
Cream together the butter and sugar

Spread this mixture on one layer of the cooled cake. Then place the second layer on top.

and add the eggs gradually, beating well.
Sift together the flour and baking powder and lightly fold into the mixture, adding the seeds and the milk as you go.
Put into a greased and floured cake tin and bake for about 1½ hours. The cake is cooked when a skewer inserted into it comes out clean. Remove from the oven and cool on a wire rack.

The ingredients for Ginger Fruit Cake (recipe page 61) include raisins and dates, honey and molasses—all high in vitamins.

THE COMPARATIVE VALUES OF FLOUR

	Wholemeal	Brown	80% extraction	White enriched
Extraction Rate	100%	90%	80%	70%
Protein %	12.00	11.80	11.50	11.10
Fat %	2.49	1.90	1.40	1.16
Carbohydrate %	64.30	67.50	70.10	72.30
Calories per 100 grams	336.00	348.00	348.00	350.00
Calcium (mg. per 100 grams	30.00	148.00	145.00	142.00
Iron (mg. per 100 grams	3.50	2.70	1.70	1.70
Thiamine (mg. per 100 grams	0.40	0.33	0.24	0.24
Niacin (mg. per 100 grams	5.70	3.50	1.60	1.60

63

grow it

Even if you have a very small garden, it is possible to grow vegetables and herbs to add variety and nutritional value to everyday meals. And for flat-dwellers an indoor herb garden or a tiny salad plot in a window-box is a practical possibility. When space is limited the best plan is to decide which vegetables will give the best return. Choose quick-growing, easy-to-care-for plants which don't need a lot of space. Spinach, for example, is not only extremely nutritious: it is also practically self-perpetuating—the more you pick it the faster it grows. But you need to plant rows and rows of cabbages to feed a family throughout the winter. And, there is no point in planting rows of potatoes and turnips if you are not going to eat them.

The three top herbs for sheer usefulness are chives, parsley and mint. Grow them from seeds indoors or buy the plants in spring. When all danger of frost is past transfer them to a sheltered outside plot or window-box. Once these hardy plants take hold, they will spread fairly rapidly. Parsley is tops for food value and can be added to very many dishes. Use chives in soups, salads and sauces. Add mint to potatoes, vegetables and healthy drinks and use chopped fresh mint as a garnish.

Lettuces, spring onions [scallions], watercress and radishes need little space and are fairly easy to care for. Tomatoes can be grown indoors. Buy the plants in spring and rear them carefully in a box on a sunny window-sill. Mushrooms can be cultivated in any dark place—the cupboard under the stairs, the cellar or even the airing cupboard. Again they are so useful that growing them is well worth while. Give back the goodness which the plants extract from the soil by using compost (in the window-box, too). You can make a small compost heap with grass cuttings, leaves, twigs, vegetable peels and outer leaves, and newspapers and cardboard (paper was once a tree, after all). Spread this over the ground about a month before planting.

If space allows, and you have time to care for them, then soft fruits are a good idea. Strawberries, raspberries, blackcurrants, redcurrants and gooseberries are all delicious and useful for their food-value.

recipe list

key to symbols

⊠ This is a guide to the preparation and cooking time required for each dish and will vary according to the skill of the individual cook.

⊠ Less than 1 hour
⊠ ⊠ Between 1 hour and 2½ hours
⊠ ⊠ ⊠ Over 2½ hours

☆ This indicates that the recipe requires no cooking

please note:

Equivalents for American ingredients are given in the text in square brackets. All weight and measure equivalents are approximate. Tablespoons and teaspoons are Standard Spoon measures and are level. For the purpose of recipe conversion, Standard British teaspoons and tablespoons are equivalent to Standard American ones.

british ingredients

american equivalents

British	American
Aubergine	Eggplant
Bacon rashers	Bacon strips
Beanshoots	Beansprouts
Beetroot	Beet
Bicarbonate of soda	Baking soda
Biscuit	Cookie
Broad bean	Lima bean
Castor sugar	Fine granulated sugar
Chicory	Endive
Cornflour	Cornstarch
Courgettes	Zucchini
Cream, double	Cream, heavy
Cream, single	Cream, light
Demerara sugar	Soft, light brown sugar
Desiccated coconut	Shredded coconut
Digestive biscuit	Graham cracker
Dry ginger	Ginger ale
Fish fingers	Fish sticks
Gammon	Raw ham
Gelatine	Gelatin
Greaseproof paper	Waxed paper
To grill	To broil
Jelly	Flavored gelatin, jello
Marrow	Squash
Minced beef	Ground beef
Pepper	Capsicum
Plain madeira cake	Pound cake
Potato chip	French fried potato
Potato crisp	Potato chip
Prawn	Shrimp
Red peppers (sweet)	Pimento
Sandwich tin	Cake tin
Scone	Biscuit
Sieve	Strainer
Silverside	Brisket
Spring greens	Collards, young cabbage
Spring onions	Scallion
Sultana	Raisin
Swede	Rutabaga
Sweet	Candy
Sweetcorn	Corn
Tart	Pie
Wholemeal bread	Wholewheat bread
100% Wholemeal flour	Wholewheat flour

metric conversion table

solid measures: equivalents

ounces	grammes	pounds	kilogrammes
1	28	1	0.45
2	57	2	0.9
3	85	3	1.4
4 (¼ lb.)	113	4	1.8
5	142	5	2.3
6	170	6	2.7
7	198	7	3.2
8 (½ lb.)	227	8	3.6
9	255	9	4.1
10	283	10	4.5
16 (1 lb.)	454		

N.B. These conversions are approximate and rounded to the nearest point

liquid measures: equivalents

British	American	Metric
⅙ fl. oz.	1 teaspoon	5 ml. approx.
½ fl. oz.	1 tablespoon	15 ml. approx.
1 fl. oz.	2 tablespoons	30 ml. approx.
8 fl. oz.	1 cup	2.27 dl.
10 fl. oz. (½ pint)	1¼ cups	3.83 dl.
16 fl. oz.	1 pint (2 cups)	4.5 dl. or .45 litre approx. ½ litre
20 fl. oz. (1 pint)	2½ cups	5.86 dl.
35 fl. oz. (2 lb. 3 oz)	4⅓ cups	10 dl. or 1 litre

Credits